# Foundation Core GCSE Maths 1–3 Homework Book

## Michael White

Elmwood Education

First published 2015 by
Elmwood Education
Unit 5
Mallow Park
Watchmead
Welwyn Garden City
Herts. AL7 1GX
Tel. 01707 333232

ISBN 9781 906 622 473

# Contents

# Unit 4

## Geometry 1

# Unit 5

## Number 3

# Unit 7

## Algebra 2

# Unit 8

## Statistics 1

# Unit 9

## Geometry 2

# Unit 10
## Statistics 2

# Unit 11
## Geometry 3

# NUMBER 1     1

**TASK M1.1/M1.2** — **Main Book Page 1**

**1** What is the value of the underlined digit in each number below:

    **a** 3<u>2</u>6     **b** <u>5</u>18     **c** 6<u>1</u>73     **d** <u>4</u>953     **e** 20<u>4</u>

**2**   5   3   4

    **a** Using all the 3 cards above, what is the *smallest* number you can make?

    **b** Using all the 3 cards above, what is the *largest* number you can make?

**3** Jamie bought a new sofa for £1350. Write down the value of the 5 digit.

**4** Annie sold her car for £5750. Write down the value of the 7 digit.

**5** The 7 in the number 24·73 means $\frac{7}{10}$. What is the value of the underlined digit in each number below:

    **a** 0·6<u>9</u>     **b** 0·4<u>37</u>     **c** 0·32<u>8</u>     **d** 0·<u>5</u>8

    **e** 9·71<u>4</u>     **f** 3·<u>6</u>28     **g** <u>23</u>·748     **h** 46·20<u>7</u>

**6** Which number is the smaller: 0·03 or 0·3 ?

    Give a reason for your answer.

**7** The number 26·7 can be written as $20 + 6 + \frac{7}{10}$.

    Write the number 49·37 in this way.

**8** Which number is the larger: 0·6 or 0·09 ?

    Give a reason for your answer.

**9** Which number is the smallest: 0·7 0·008 0·06 ?

**10** A number can be written as $40 + 8 + \frac{9}{100}$.

    Write this number as a decimal.

**TASK M1.3/M1.4** — **Main Book Page 3**

**1** Round to the nearest 10.

    **a** 38     **b** 43     **c** 84     **d** 75     **e** 328

**2** Round to the nearest 100.

    **a** 340     **b** 764     **c** 350     **d** 1240     **e** 1550

**3** Round to the nearest 1000.

    **a** 3700     **b** 5550     **c** 7143     **d** 4238     **e** 6500

**4** Carl has £13·64. Round this to the nearest pound.

**5** Maria weighs 54·37 kg. Round this to the nearest kilogram.

**6** Round to the nearest whole number.

    **a** 6·8     **b** 4·5     **c** 7·6     **d** 13·2     **e** 18·5

**7** Work out these answers *with a calculator* and then round off the answers to the *nearest whole number*.

    **a** 7·1 × 3·89     **b** 6·31 × 4·75     **c** 5·08 × 3·17     **d** 693 ÷ 19

    **e** 512 ÷ 4·67     **f** 71·4 ÷ 5·26     **g** 5·61 ÷ 13     **h** 6·82 × 1·78

**8** One evening around 300 people visit a nightclub. This number is rounded off to the nearest 100. Which of the numbers below could be the exact number of people at the nightclub?

    260     349     249     359     302     393     287     238

**9** Round off 16 456 to

    **a** the nearest 10     **b** the nearest 100     **c** the nearest 1000.

**10** Dougal says that he has saved £3200. He has rounded off this money to the nearest £100. What is the least amount of money that Dougal may have saved?

---

**TASK M1.5/M1.6**          **Main Book Page 6**

*Do not use a calculator.*

Copy and complete.

**1**
```
  4 7
+ 6 4
```

**2**
```
  5 6 4
+ 2 3 9
```

**3**
```
  3 1 2 7
+ 4 3 8 6
```

**4**
```
  6 4
- 3 7
```

**5**
```
  8 3
- 4 8
```

**6**
```
  4 8 1
- 2 6 4
```

**7**
```
  5 9 8
- 3 1 9
```

**8**
```
  4 6 2 8
- 1 3 8 6
```

**9**
```
  6 2 1 7
- 4 4 0 6
```

**10**
```
  3 8 7 4 2
+ 1 2 6 3 8
```

**11** 387 + 519     **12** 462 − 181     **13** 1374 − 648

**14** Hannah has saved £415. She wants to buy a music centre costing £694. How much more money must she save?

**15** The following people collect money for a Cancer charity.

| Ellie £138 | Dan £193 | Shalina £68 |
|---|---|---|
| Katie £89 | Callum £47 | Jack £204 |

How much money have they collected in total?

**16** Find the difference between 592 and 176.

**17** Marcus is taking part in a 1290 mile car rally. He has completed 863 miles.
How many more miles must he cover?

**18**
> Tin of beans
> 48p each
> Buy 1 and get
> 1 half price

How many tins of beans
can I buy with £5?
Show all your working
out clearly.

Copy and complete questions **19** to **24** by writing the missing number in the box.

**19** $360 + \boxed{\phantom{00}} = 589$

**20** $270 + \boxed{\phantom{00}} = 440$

**21** $348 - \boxed{\phantom{00}} = 230$

**22** $712 - \boxed{\phantom{00}} = 508$

**23** $1365 - \boxed{\phantom{00}} = 980$

**24** $\boxed{\phantom{00}} - 286 = 461$

**25** How many packs of
toilet rolls can I buy
with £10?

*Explain your answer fully.*

> Pack of 4 toilet rolls
> £2·10
> Buy 1 and get 1 free

---

**TASK M1.7** | **Main Book Page 8**

*Do not use a calculator.*

**1** Work out

   **a** $72 \times 100$

   **b** $4160 \times 10$

   **c** $586\,000 \div 10$

   **d** $673\,000 \div 100$

   **e** $570 \times 100$

   **f** $6720 \times 1000$

**2** Copy and complete

   **a** $\boxed{\phantom{00}} \div 100 = 47$

   **b** $\boxed{\phantom{00}} \times 100 = 3800$

   **c** $\boxed{\phantom{00}} \times 10 = 4800$

   **d** $160 \times \boxed{\phantom{00}} = 16\,000$

   **e** $36\,000 \div \boxed{\phantom{00}} = 3600$

   **f** $\boxed{\phantom{00}} \times 100 = 72\,000$

   **g**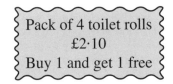

**3** A group of 100 people won £8 000 000 on the National Lottery.
How much money did each person win if they each received an equal share?

**4** Work out

   **a** $20 \times 60$

   **b** $900 \times 30$

   **c** $1500 \div 30$

   **d** $6400 \div 800$

   **e** $36\,000 \div 90$

   **f** $400 \times 700$

**5** 30 houses each costing £90 000 are built on a housing estate.
What is the *total* cost of all 30 houses?

**6** Copy and complete

    **a** $\boxed{\phantom{00}} \times 40 = 3200$      **b** $\boxed{\phantom{00}} \times 200 = 8000$      **c** $\boxed{\phantom{00}} \times 90 = 540$

    **d** $\boxed{\phantom{00}} \div 50 = 60$      **e** $72\,000 \div \boxed{\phantom{00}} = 90$      **f** $\boxed{\phantom{00}} \div 300 = 70$

**7** 'Caravans Я Us' sell a Highbridge caravan for £19 000 and a Carlton caravan for £24 000.
During one year they sell 40 Highbridge caravans and 20 Carlton caravans.
Work out the total amount of money for these caravan sales.
How much more than a million pounds is this?

**8** Copy and complete

$$\boxed{600} \rightarrow \boxed{\div 20} \rightarrow \boxed{\phantom{00}} \rightarrow \boxed{\times 40} \rightarrow \boxed{\phantom{00}} \rightarrow \boxed{\times 20} \rightarrow \boxed{\phantom{00}} \rightarrow \boxed{\div 60} \rightarrow \boxed{\phantom{00}}$$

---

**TASK M1.8**                           **Main Book Page 10**

*Do not use a calculator.*

Copy and complete.

**1**   $\begin{array}{r} 4\ 2 \\ \times\ 4 \\ \hline \end{array}$      **2**   $\begin{array}{r} 6\ 3 \\ \times\ 5 \\ \hline \end{array}$      **3**   $\begin{array}{r} 3\ 7 \\ \times\ 8 \\ \hline \end{array}$      **4**   $49 \times 3$      **5**   $6 \times 84$

**6**   $\begin{array}{r} 3\ 0\ 4 \\ \times\ 3 \\ \hline \end{array}$      **7**   $\begin{array}{r} 5\ 2\ 6 \\ \times\ 4 \\ \hline \end{array}$      **8**   $\begin{array}{r} 4\ 6\ 3 \\ \times\ 8 \\ \hline \end{array}$      **9**   $738 \times 6$      **10**   $9 \times 284$

**11** 629 students at a school each pay £6 to go on a school trip.
How much money do they pay *in total*?

**12** Each month Kabir's grandparents give him £5.
How much do they give him during two years?

**13** Work out $68 \times 7 \times 4$

**14** An adult must pay £9 to see a pantomime and a child must pay £6.
During one performance there are 48 adults and 72 children.
Work out the total amount of money paid.

**15** Which is larger – $\boxed{38 \times 6 \times 8}$ or $\boxed{49 \times 4 \times 9}$?

---

**TASK M1.9**                           **Main Book Page 11**

*Do not use a calculator.*

Work out without a calculator.

**1**   $32 \times 14$      **2**   $17 \times 24$      **3**   $42 \times 23$      **4**   $64 \times 34$

**5**   $213 \times 15$      **6**   $421 \times 36$      **7**   $839 \times 28$      **8**   $627 \times 56$

**9** Gary sells 37 shirts at £16 each.
How much money does Gary receive in total?

**10** At the World Cup there were 24 teams. If each team had a squad of 26 players,
how many players were there *in total*?

**11** 46 football supporters are travelling to an away match. They each pay £64 for a ticket.
22 supporters travel by train and the rest travel by coach.
How much money do they spend in total on travelling
to the game and the match tickets?

| coach ticket | £16 |
|---|---|
| train ticket | £34 |

**12** 36 people dine at a restaurant and each pay £23.
It costs the restaurant £415 to prepare and serve the food.
How much profit does the restaurant make?

---

**TASK M1.10** ························· **Main Book Page 12**

*Do not use a calculator.*

Work out

**1** 48 ÷ 6   **2** 28 ÷ 4   **3** 36 ÷ 9   **4** 72 ÷ 8   **5** 56 ÷ 7

**6** 3)69   **7** 4)136   **8** 6)438   **9** 8)296   **10** 7)1512

**11** 384 ÷ 8   **12** 354 ÷ 6   **13** 375 ÷ 5   **14** 2457 ÷ 7   **15** 2898 ÷ 6

---

**TASK M1.11** ························· **Main Book Page 13**

Work out each answer, giving the remainder.

**1** 4)583   **2** 5)712   **3** 8)316   **4** 6)2715   **5** 9)4814

**6** 828 ÷ 7   **7** 486 ÷ 5   **8** 377 ÷ 8   **9** 4386 ÷ 7   **10** 7245 ÷ 4

**11** 43 children are playing in a 5-a-side tournament.
How many complete teams of 5 players can be made?

**12** A calculator costs £7. How many calculators can a school buy for £225?

**13** A wine box at a supermarket can hold 6 bottles.
How many boxes are needed to hold 112 bottles?

**14** Maria sells boxes of candles for £6·99 each. Each box contains 8 candles.
Maria has 197 candles to sell. She sells all the boxes that she can fill up and sells the leftover
candles for 75p each. Work out the total amount of money that she receives.

6

*Do not use a calculator.*

Work out

**1** 448 ÷ 16      **2** 612 ÷ 17      **3** 575 ÷ 23      **4** 576 ÷ 36

**5** 986 ÷ 29      **6** 774 ÷ 18      **7** 988 ÷ 26      **8** 722 ÷ 38

**9** A book of stamps contains 36 stamps. How many books must I buy if I need 850 stamps?

**10** 1500 sweets are shared equally into 46 packets. How many sweets will be in each packet and how many sweets will be left over?

**11** Which answer is the odd one out?

| 891 ÷ 33 | 406 ÷ 14 | 648 ÷ 24 |

A               B               C

**12** One coach may carry 47 people. How many coaches are needed to transport 560 football fans to an away match?

**13** 37 screws are used to make a flat pack desk. If a factory has 623 screws remaining, how many flat packs could the factory supply?

**14** 15 people pay a total of £7005 for a holiday. 14 of the people pay a total of £6356 and each pays the same amount. How much more does the 15th person pay than each of the other people?

**1**
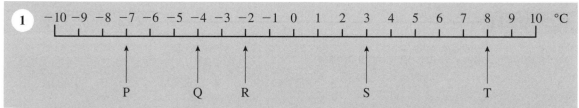

The *difference* in temperature between Q and R is 2 °C. Give the difference in temperature between:

**a** R and S      **b** Q and S      **c** R and T      **d** P and T

**2** The temperature in Liverpool is −3 °C and the temperature in Plymouth is 2 °C.
How much *warmer* is Plymouth than Liverpool?

**3** The temperature in Hull is −1 °C. The temperature rises by 8 °C.
What is the new temperature in Hull?

**4** Work out

**a** 2 − 7      **b** −3 − 2      **c** −4 + 1      **d** −9 − 2      **e** −6 + 5

**5** What is the *difference* between the two smallest numbers below?

$$4 \qquad -6 \qquad -3 \qquad 1 \qquad 5 \qquad -4$$

---

**TASK M1.15** ———————————————————————— **Main Book Page 18**

**1** Work out

**a** $5 - -3$ **b** $7 + -4$ **c** $-2 - 3$ **d** $-5 - 1$ **e** $-6 + 2$

**f** $-7 - -1$ **g** $-4 - -4$ **h** $-3 + -6$ **i** $-2 + -6$ **j** $-6 - -6$

**2** Copy and complete the boxes below:

**a** $3 - \boxed{\phantom{x}} = -5$ **b** $\boxed{\phantom{x}} - 1 = -4$ **c** $-9 + \boxed{\phantom{x}} = -3$

**d** $\boxed{\phantom{x}} - -4 = -2$ **e** $-4 - \boxed{\phantom{x}} = -10$ **f** $\boxed{\phantom{x}} + -7 = -5$

**3** Paula owes £75 to her bank. She repays £115 then spends £62 from her bank account. How much does she now owe the bank?

**4** Which question below gives a different answer to the other two?

$$\boxed{A \quad -5 - 3} \qquad \boxed{B \quad -9 - -2} \qquad \boxed{C \quad -10 + 2}$$

**5** Work out

**a** $-4 + 2 - 3$ **b** $-1 - 6 + 4$ **c** $-9 + 6 - -1$

**d** $-2 + -3 + -4$ **e** $-8 - -6 + -3$ **f** $-3 - 9 - -4 - 2$

---

**TASK M1.16/M1.17** ———————————————————— **Main Book Page 20**

**1** Work out

**a** $6 \times -4$ **b** $-3 \times 8$

**c** $-2 \times -4$ **d** $-10 \div 2$

**e** $-28 \div -4$ **f** $-30 \div -5$

**g** $-7 \times -6$ **h** $-9 \times 8$

**i** $48 \div -6$ **j** $-6 \times 9$

**k** $-35 \div 7$ **l** $-30 \div 6$

**m** $-81 \div -9$ **n** $-7 \times -8$

**o** $-3 \times -3 \times -3$ **p** $-9 \times 4 \times -2$

**q** $5 \times -6 \times 2$ **r** $-4 \times 5 \times -3 \times -2$

**2** Copy and complete the multiplication square below:

| $\times$ | $-4$ | | $-8$ | |
|---|---|---|---|---|
| 3 | $-12$ | | | |
| | | | 40 | $-45$ |
| | $-24$ | $-12$ | | |
| | | | 24 | |

Each empty square below contains either a number or an operation ($+$, $-$, $\times$, $\div$).
Copy each square and fill in the missing details. The arrows are equals signs.

**3**

| 16 | ÷ |  | → | −4 |
|---|---|---|---|---|
| ÷ |  | × |  |  |
| −8 | + | 5 | → |  |
| ↓ |  | ↓ |  |  |
|  | × |  | → |  |

**4**

| −3 | × |  | → | 12 |
|---|---|---|---|---|
|  |  | × |  |  |
| −7 | − | −6 | → |  |
| ↓ |  | ↓ |  |  |
| 21 | − |  | → |  |

**5**

| −15 | + | −5 | → |  |
|---|---|---|---|---|
| ÷ |  | × |  |  |
|  |  |  | → | −3 |
| ↓ |  | ↓ |  |  |
| 3 |  | −10 | → | 13 |

---

**TASK M1.18/M1.19** — **Main Book Page 22**

**1** Work out

| | | | |
|---|---|---|---|
| **a** $6 + 4 \times 2$ | **b** $5 + 2 \times 3$ | **c** $(3 + 2) \times 6$ | **d** $32 \div 4 + 6$ |
| **e** $4 \times 7 + 3$ | **f** $30 \div (4 + 1)$ | **g** $6 \times (9 - 3)$ | **h** $5 + 6 \times 3 + 2$ |
| **i** $(5 + 4) \div 3 + 7$ | **j** $(5 + 7) \div (6 - 2)$ | **k** $28 - 3 \times 6$ | **l** $4 + 6 \times 2 \div 2$ |
| **m** $(8 - 3) \times (4 + 5)$ | **n** $(8 + 3 + 9) \div 5$ | **o** $36 \div (2 + 7)$ | **p** $(4 + 16) \div (8 - 3)$ |

**2** Copy each question and write brackets so that each calculation gives the correct answer.

| | | |
|---|---|---|
| **a** $7 \times 4 + 2 = 42$ | **b** $6 + 9 \div 3 = 5$ | **c** $6 + 3 \times 4 = 36$ |
| **d** $4 + 3 \times 8 - 6 = 14$ | **e** $12 + 6 \div 9 = 2$ | **f** $15 - 6 \times 3 + 6 = 81$ |
| **g** $8 \times 4 - 2 = 16$ | **h** $72 \div 2 + 6 = 9$ | |

**3** $7 \times (\square - 2) = 26 - 10 \div 2$    What number belongs in the box?

**4** $(4 + 2) \times (7 - 3) = 8 + \square \times 4$    What number belongs in the box?

**5** Work out

| | | |
|---|---|---|
| **a** $28 + 12 \times 3$ | **b** $(28 + 12) \times 3$ | **c** $63 - 14 \times 3$ |
| **d** $21 + 20 \div 2$ | **e** $56 \div (3 + 5)$ | **f** $(13 + 17) \times (62 - 12)$ |
| **g** $4 + 16 \times 5$ | **h** $50 - 100 \div 4$ | **i** $72 \div 8 - 32 \div 4$ |
| **j** $28 + 48 \div 12$ | **k** $31 - 9 \times 3 + 16$ | **l** $39 + 63 \div 7$ |

---

**TASK M1.20/M1.21** — **Main Book Page 24**

**1** $3^2 = 3 \times 3 = 9$. Find the value of

**a** $5^2$    **b** $7^2$    **c** $6^2$    **d** $1^2$    **e** $30^2$

**2** $\sqrt{49} = 7$ because $7 \times 7 = 49$. Find the value of

**a** $\sqrt{16}$    **b** $\sqrt{36}$    **c** $\sqrt{100}$    **d** $\sqrt{64}$    **e** $\sqrt{1}$

**3** What is the length of one side of this square?

area = 25 cm²

**4** Write down the square root of 400.

**5** Find the value of

a $3^2 + 4^2$      b $9^2 - 4^2$      c $(8 - 2)^2$

d $10^2 + 6^2$      e $\sqrt{81} - \sqrt{4}$      f $\sqrt{16} + \sqrt{25}$

g $\sqrt{(28 + 21)}$      h $\sqrt{(63 - 59)}$      i $\sqrt{(6^2 + 8^2)}$

**6** Is 90 a square number? Explain your answer.

**7** Jarvis multiplies a square number by 4 and gets another square number. Write down what these two square numbers might be.

**8** $7^3 = 7 \times 7 \times 7 = 49 \times 7 = 343$. Find the value of

a $2^3$      b $4^3$      c $1^3$      d $5^3$      e $10^3$

**9** How many small cubes are needed to make this giant cube?

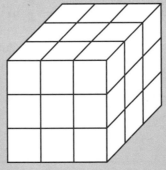

**10** $\sqrt[3]{64} = 4$ because $4 \times 4 \times 4 = 64$. Find the value of

a $\sqrt[3]{8}$      b $\sqrt[3]{1}$      c $\sqrt[3]{125}$      d $\sqrt[3]{27}$

**11** Write down the cube root of 1000.

**12** Find the value of

a $\sqrt[3]{(5 + 3)}$      b $\sqrt[3]{(6^2 + 4^2 + 12)}$      c $(3^2 - 2^2)^3$

---

**TASK M1.22**                     **Main Book Page 27**

**1** $4 \times 4 \times 4 \times 4 \times 4$ means '4 to the power 5' which is written as $4^5$ (*index form*). Write the following in index form.

a $3 \times 3 \times 3 \times 3$      b $2 \times 2 \times 2 \times 2 \times 2 \times 2$      c $7 \times 7 \times 7 \times 7 \times 7$      d $10 \times 10 \times 10$

**2** $3^5$ means $3 \times 3 \times 3 \times 3 \times 3$. Copy and complete the following:

   **a** $9^4$ means ........................        **b** $5^4$ means ........................

   **c** $6^6$ means ........................        **d** $2^7$ means ........................

**3** Which is smaller? $\boxed{3^2}$ or $\boxed{2^3}$

**4** Which is smaller? $\boxed{5^2}$ or $\boxed{2^5}$

**5** Find the value of

   **a** $2 \times 3^2$           **b** $3^3 \times 4$           **c** $5^3 \times 2^2$

**6** Robyn has 4 gerbils. Each month the number of gerbils increases by 4 times the amount of gerbils at the start of the month. How many gerbils does Robyn have after 3 months?

**7** Work out $\sqrt{(7 \times 7 \times 5 \times 5)}$ without using a calculator.

Use a calculator for the questions below:

**8** Find the value of

   **a** $5^4$           **b** $3^6$           **c** $4 \times 4 \times 4 \times 4 \times 4$     **d** $10^5$

   **e** $7^5$           **f** $2^{12}$          **g** 6 to the power 7       **h** $3 \times 3 \times 3 \times 3 \times 3$

   **i** $8 \times 8 \times 8 \times 8$    **j** $3^8$          **k** $4^7$             **l** 8 to the power 6

**9** Write down the next two numbers in this sequence:

   3,  9,  27,  81,  243,  ......,  ......

**10** How many numbers are in the sequence below up to and including 512?

   2,  4,  8,  16,  ...........,  512

---

**TASK M1.23/M1.24**                                  **Main Book Page 29**

Write down *all* the factors of the following numbers:

**1**  20 (6 factors)        **2**  12 (6 factors)        **3**  29 (2 factors)

**4**  18                 **5**  32                **6**  50

**7**  Which of these numbers are:

   **a**  even numbers?       **b**  odd numbers?

   **c**  prime numbers?     **d**  factors of 24?

2, 13, 11, 5, 6, 9, 14

**8**  Write down *all* the *even* factors of 24.

9　Write down *all* the factors of 35 which are *prime*.

10　Which numbers between 30 and 40 have 4 as a factor?

11　Write down the first 5 multiples of:
   a 3　　　b 6　　　c 9　　　d 8　　　e 12

12　Which of these numbers are:
   a multiples of 6
   b multiples of 7
   c *not* multiples of 2

   18　54
   21　63　26
   42　28

13　Copy and complete the first five multiples of 6 and 10.

   <u>6</u>:　6　12　☐　☐　☐
   <u>10</u>:　10　☐　☐　☐　☐

   Write down the <u>L</u>owest <u>C</u>ommon <u>M</u>ultiple of 6 and 10.

14　Find the Lowest Common Multiple of each of these pairs of numbers.
   a 5 and 8　　　b 8 and 12　　　c 10 and 60

15　Which numbers between 60 and 75 have 8 as a factor?

16　Amy and Josh are racing each other. Amy takes 5 minutes to complete one lap.
   Josh takes 7 minutes to complete one lap. After how many minutes will Amy and Josh pass
   the starting point at exactly the same time?

17　Jess thinks of a number which is greater than 60 and is a multiple of 6.
   She adds 28 onto this number to give the 10th largest square number.
   What number did Jess think of?

---

**TASK M1.25**　　　　　　　　　　　　　　　　　　　　**Main Book Page 32**

1　a List all the factors of 18.
   b List all the factors of 30.
   c Write down the <u>H</u>ighest <u>C</u>ommon <u>F</u>actor of 18 and 30.

2　a List all the factors of 30.
   b List all the factors of 45.
   c Write down the Highest Common Factor of 30 and 45.

3　Find the Highest Common Factor of:
   a 20 and 50　　　b 25 and 60　　　c 36 and 60　　　d 16, 32 and 40

**4** Sophia says that the Lowest Common Multiple of 3 and 5 is less than the Highest Common Factor of 36 and 54. Hayden thinks that this is not true.
Who is correct? Explain your answer fully.

**5** List all the factors of the Highest Common Factor of 24 and 30.

**TASK M1.26**                                                                                    **Main Book Page 34**

**1** Work out
   **a** $3 \times 3 \times 5$          **b** $2^2 \times 7$          **c** $2^2 \times 3^2$

**2** For each question below, find the number which belongs in the empty box:
   **a** $84 = 2^2 \times 3 \times \boxed{\phantom{0}}$     **b** $40 = 2^3 \times \boxed{\phantom{0}}$     **c** $126 = 2 \times 3^2 \times \boxed{\phantom{0}}$

**3** Copy and complete these factor trees:

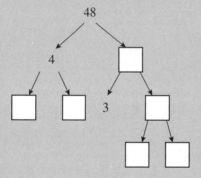

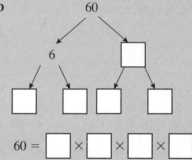

$$60 = \boxed{\phantom{0}} \times \boxed{\phantom{0}} \times \boxed{\phantom{0}} \times \boxed{\phantom{0}}$$

$$48 = 3 \times \boxed{\phantom{0}} \times \boxed{\phantom{0}} \times \boxed{\phantom{0}} \times \boxed{\phantom{0}}$$

**4** Using any method, write the following numbers as products of prime factors:
   **a** 75          **b** 44          **c** 80          **d** 594

**5** $\boxed{1617 = 3 \times 7 \times 7 \times 11}$ and $\boxed{273 = 3 \times 7 \times 13}$
   Find the Highest Common Factor of 273 and 1617.

**6** Write 315 and 495 as products of prime factors.
   Use this to find the Highest Common Factor of 315 and 495.

**7** Write 396 and 420 as products of prime factors.
   Use this to find the Highest Common Factor of 396 and 420.

**Remember:**

A standard form number will have the form $A \times 10^n$ where $1 \leqslant A < 10$

$$5600 = 5.6 \times 10^3$$
$$784\,000 = 7.84 \times 10^5$$
$$0.0053 = 5.3 \times 10^{-3}$$

standard form

**1** Copy each statement below and fill in the empty boxes.

**a** $63000 = 6.3 \times 10^\square$

**b** $5960 = 5.96 \times 10^\square$

**c** $0.096 = 9.6 \times 10^\square$

**d** $0.00058 = 5.8 \times 10^\square$

**e** $7800000 = 7.8 \times 10^\square$

**f** $0.4 = 4 \times 10^\square$

**2** Write the numbers below in standard form:

**a** 3000     **b** 70000     **c** 340     **d** 89000

**e** 0.004     **f** 0.0007     **g** 0.9     **h** 0.0018

**3** $3700 = 37 \times 10^2$. Explain why this number is not written in standard form.

**4** $28000 = 28 \times 10^3$. This number is not written in standard form.
Write it correctly in standard form.

**5** Write each number below as an ordinary number.

**a** $6 \times 10^4$     **b** $3 \times 10^2$     **c** $3 \times 10^{-2}$     **d** $5.6 \times 10^4$

**e** $2.4 \times 10^5$     **f** $8.6 \times 10^{-3}$     **g** $4.16 \times 10^3$     **h** $7.68 \times 10^{-1}$

**6** Which number below is the smaller:

$\boxed{4.7 \times 10^2}$ or $\boxed{4.7 \times 10^3}$ ?

Explain your answer fully.

**7** Which number below is larger:

$\boxed{6.5 \times 10^{-2}}$ or $\boxed{6.5 \times 10^{-3}}$ ?

Explain your answer fully.

**8** Write the numbers below in standard form.

**a** 0.0007     **b** 53000     **c** 0.096     **d** 0.487

**e** 49000000     **f** 576000     **g** 0.00074     **h** 82.4

**i** 0.1     **j** 0.000000864     **k** 6180000     **l** 42000000

**1** Use a calculator to work out the following and write each answer in standard form.

**a** $(2.6 \times 10^8) \times (7 \times 10^{10})$

**b** $(4.5 \times 10^{11}) + (3.6 \times 10^{12})$

**c** $(8 \times 10^{25}) - (4 \times 10^{24})$

**d** $(3 \times 10^{28}) \div (6 \times 10^{13})$

**2** Find the area of this rectangle, leaving your answer in standard form.

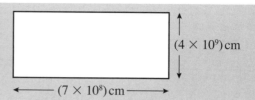

$(4 \times 10^9)$ cm

$(7 \times 10^8)$ cm

**3** The population of the UK is $(5 \cdot 97 \times 10^7)$ people.
The population of the USA is $(2 \cdot 41 \times 10^8)$ people.
What is the combined population of the UK and USA? (Give your answer in standard form.)

**4** $E = mgh$. Find the value of $E$ in standard form if $m = 4 \times 10^7$, $g = 9 \cdot 8$ and $h = 5 \times 10^6$.

**5** Five people have collected some money for charity. The amounts are shown in the table below.

| Brianna | Matt | Brooke | Vanya | Carter |
|---|---|---|---|---|
| £$(4 \cdot 116 \times 10^2)$ | £$(3 \cdot 02 \times 10^2)$ | £$(1 \cdot 01 \times 10^3)$ | £$(4 \cdot 3 \times 10)$ | £$(1 \cdot 002 \times 10^3)$ |

**a** List the names in the order of the money they each collected, starting with the greatest amount.

**b** How much more money did Carter collect than Matt?

**c** How much money did the five people collect in total?

**6** Use a calculator to work out the following and write each answer in standard form.

**a** $(4 \times 10^{-10}) \times (9 \times 10^{-6})$

**b** $\dfrac{8 \times 10^{13}}{4 \times 10^{-8}}$

**c** $(5 \times 10^{-22}) \times \sqrt{(1 \cdot 6 \times 10^{11})}$

**d** $(9 \times 10^{-15}) - (7 \times 10^{-16})$

**e** $\dfrac{(5 \times 10^{17}) \times (3 \times 10^{12})}{4 \times 10^{-7}}$

**f** $\dfrac{(4 \times 10^9)^2}{2 \times 10^{-8}}$

**7** The mass of an atom is $3 \cdot 74 \times 10^{-26}$ grams.
What is the total mass of 2 million atoms?

**8** The adult population of a country is 60 million.
The amount of money earned by each adult is £27 000.
Find in standard form the total money earned by the entire adult population.

**9** The acceleration $a$ of a particle is given by the formula

$$a = \frac{v - u}{t}.$$

Work out the value of $a$ when $v = 3 \times 10^{14}$, $u = 5 \times 10^{13}$ and $t = 5 \times 10^3$.

**1** Trinity has £$n$. Nikita has £15 more than Trinity. Sophie has twice as much money as Trinity. Write down an expression, in terms of $n$, for

**a** Sophie's money

**b** Nikita's money

**c** The total amount of money that all three people have.

**2** A pot of yoghurt costs 49p and a pint of milk costs 54p. Write down an expression for the cost of

**a** $m$ pots of yoghurt

**b** $n$ pints of milk

**c** the total cost of $m$ pots of yoghurt and $n$ pints of milk.

**3** In a game of rugby, 5 points are scored for a try, 2 points for a conversion and 3 points for a penalty. In a match Aron Vale rugby team scores $x$ tries, $y$ penalties and $m$ conversions. Write down an expression for the total number of points scored by Aron Vale.

**4** The table below shows the weights of five people in kilograms, in increasing order of size.

| Mason | Julia | Andrew | Jiang | Elena |
|-------|-------|--------|-------|-------|
| $x$   | $y$   | 62     | $m$   | $n$   |

Write down an expression for:

**a** how much more Elena weighs than Julia

**b** the total weight of Andrew, Jiang and Elena

**c** Mason's weight if he loses 3 kg

**d** the difference in weight between Jiang and Andrew.

**5** A concert ticket costs £16 for an adult and £9 for a child.

**a** Write down an expression for the total cost of the tickets for $n$ adults and $y$ children.

**b** If all children get their tickets half price, write down a new expression for the total cost of the tickets for $n$ adults and $y$ children.

**6** Gavin sells jackets for £$n$ each. During one week he sells 15 jackets. He spends £$m$ on food. He saves half of the remaining money. Write down an expression for the amount of money he saves.

16

In questions **1** to **20** find the value of each expression when $p = 4$

$q = 3$

$r = 7$

**1**  $3p$

**2**  $qr$

**3**  $5p + 7$

**4**  $2p + 5r$

**5**  $8q - 2r$

**6**  $p^2$

**7**  $r - 2q$

**8**  $r^2$

**9**  $q^2 + r^2$

**10**  $8(p - q)$

**11**  $9(2r - p)$

**12**  $q(6p + 2q)$

**13**  $r(3r - 4q)$

**14**  $\dfrac{8q}{p}$

**15**  $9q + 6$

**16**  $\dfrac{2p + 2q}{r}$

**17**  $\dfrac{6(p + q)}{r}$

**18**  $p^2 + q^2 + r^2$

**19**  $pqr$

**20**  $5p + 6q - 3r$

In questions **21** to **23** find the value of each expression:

**21**  $20 - 2y$ if $y = 5$

**22**  $9(3a + 1)$ if $a = 2$

**23**  $8m + m^2$ if $m = 4$

In questions **1** to **20** find the value of each expression when $f = -1$

$g\ p = 5$

$h = -4$

**1**  $2h$

**2**  $3f$

**3**  $fg$

**4**  $fh$

**5**  $2g - h$

**6**  $3f + 4g$

**7**  $4f + 3g$

**8**  $h^2$

**9**  $g^2 + h^2$

**10**  $16 - h$

**11**  $f + g + h$

**12**  $5g + 6f$

**13**  $6h + 10$

**14**  $3(f + g)$

**15**  $7(g - f)$

**16**  $(4f)^2$

**17**  $4g - 3f + 3h$

**18**  $\dfrac{6h}{2f}$

**19**  $\dfrac{7(f + g)}{h}$

**20**  $2h^2$

In questions **21** to **23** find the value of each expression:

**21**  $3b + 6$ if $b = -2$

**22**  $4(2 - 3x)$ if $x = -6$

**23**  $9(n^2 - 20)$ if $n = -5$

**1**  $c = 4d - 3$

Find $c$ when $d = 5$.

**2**  $y = 5x + 6$

Find $y$ when $x = 7$.

**3**  $m = \dfrac{p}{4} - 8$

Find $m$ when $p = 40$.

**4**  $A = 6(B + 2)$

Find $A$ when $B = 7$.

**5**  $V = IR$

Find $V$ when $I = 7$ and $R = 15$.

**6**  $f = \dfrac{2u}{v}$

Find $f$ when $u = 16$ and $v = 4$.

**7**  $y = 5(2x + 6y)$

Find $y$ when $x = 4$ and $y = 7$.

**8**  $P = \dfrac{Q}{6} + 4R$

Find $P$ when $Q = 48$ and $R = 13$.

**9**  $A = r^2 + wr$

*Use a calculator* to find the value of $A$ when $r = 3·6$ and $w = 1·4$.

**10**  $V = lwh + 4wh$

*Use a calculator* to find the value of $V$ when $l = 8·4$, $w = 0·9$ and $h = 3·8$.

---

**TASK E2.2** ──────────────────────────── **Main Book Page 54**

**1**  Below are several different formulas for $p$ in terms of $n$. Find the value of $p$ in each case.

**a**  $p = 8n + 7$      when $n = 0·5$

**b**  $p = 6(4n - 1)$   when $n = 5$

**c**  $p = \dfrac{3n}{2} + n^2$     when $n = 6$

**2**  The total surface area $A$ of this cuboid is given by the formula $A = 2lw + 2lh + 2hw$

Find the value of $A$ when

**a**  $l = 5$,   $w = 3$    and   $h = 1$

**b**  $l = 10$,  $w = 2·5$   and   $h = 4$

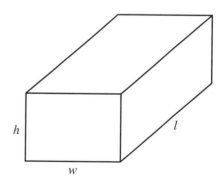

**3**  Find the value of $y$ using formulas and values given below:

**a**  $y = 4x + c$     when $x = 17$ and $c = -3$

**b**  $y = x^2 - b$     when $x = -3$ and $b = 2$

**c**  $y = \dfrac{x}{9} + \dfrac{z}{4}$     when $x = 54$ and $z = 68$

**d**  $y = x^2 + 8x$     when $x = -10$

18

**4** The surface area $A$ of a sphere is given by the
formula $A = 12r^2$
Find the value of $A$ when

**a** $r = 3$ **b** $r = 5$ **c** $r = 8$

**5** Energy $E$ is given by the formula $E = mc^2$ where $m$ is the mass and $c$ is the speed of light.
Find the value of $E$ when $m = 15$ and $c = 300\,000\,000$.

**6** Using the formula $M = 7P - Q$, find the value of $M$ when

**a** $P = -8$ and $Q = 19$ **b** $P = -15$ and $Q = -88$

**7** Using the formula $a = \dfrac{v - u}{t}$, find the value of $a$ when $v = 6.9$, $u = -2.4$ and $t = 0.2$

| **TASK M2.4** | **Main Book Page 56** |

Collect like terms

**1** $9x + 4y + 5y$

**2** $5p + 6q + 3p$

**3** $8a + 2b + 4b + 5a$

**4** $4m - 2m + 8p + p$

**5** $4a + 6b - b$

**6** $4f + 3f + 6g - 5f$

**7** $3a + 6b + 3b - 4b$

**8** $9p - 4p + q$

**9** $4m + 6q - 3q - 2m$

**10** $5a + 8b - 7b - 4a$

**11** $2x - x + 6y - y$

**12** $5m + 2p - 3m + 9q - p$

**13** Copy and complete the pyramids below.
The answer for each box is found by adding the 2 boxes below it.

**a**

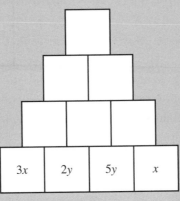

**b**

**c**

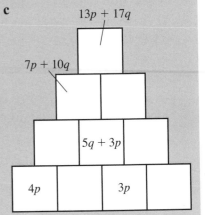

Simplify

**1** $-5b + 2b$

**2** $-4x + 9x$

**3** $-7y + 5y$

**4** $3p - 6p + 9q$

**5** $4a + 7b - b - 6a$

**6** $5x + 2 + 3x$

**7** $5c + 2 - 8c + 1$

**8** $6 + 3m - 5m$

**9** $3f + 6f + 4$

**10** $7a^2 + 3a^2 + 5a^2$

**11** $8x^2 - 6x^2 + x^2$

**12** $5ab + 10ab - 7ab$

**13** $12xy + 3x - 6xy$

**14** $9mn + 4 + 3mn$

**15** $6p^2 - p$

**16** $5m^2 - 3m + 4m^2$

**17** $a + b + ab + 4a$

**18** $4a^2 + 6ab - 4ab + 3a^2$

**19** Chen says $6n^2 + 3n + n^2$ simplifies to $9n^4$.
Bella gets an answer of $7n^2 + 3n$.
Explain clearly who is correct.

**20** Write two algebraic expressions that simplify to $9x^2$. (For example: $6x^2 + 5x^2 - 2x^2$)

**21** Write two algebraic expressions that simplify to $7m + 8$.

**22** The expression in each bag shows how much money is in it.
Find and simplify an expression for the money
Jack spends if he uses all the money in:

**a** bags A and B

**b** bags A and C

**c** all 3 bags

$6pq + 3$     $2 - 4pq$     $8p + 4$

    A        B        C

**23** Ben has £$(n^2 + 5n)$. He spends £$(4n)$.
Write down an expression for how much money he has now.

**24**

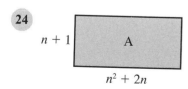

$n + 1$    A

$n^2 + 2n$

Rectangle B has a longer
perimeter than rectangle A.
Write down an expression
for how much longer the
rectangle B perimeter is.

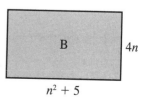

B    $4n$

$n^2 + 5$

**25** Darryl is $(4a^2 + 6ab)$ years old.
Christine is $(3a + 2ab)$ years old and Rory is $(ab - a^2)$ years old.
Find and simplify an expression for their *total* ages.

**TASK M2.6**

Do the following multiplications and divisions:

**1** $3a \times 3$    **2** $2b \times 4$    **3** $7m \times 3$    **4** $5 \times 7n$

**5** $6 \times 8y$    **6** $16x \div 2$    **7** $27y \div 3$    **8** $60a \div 10$

**9** $12b \div 4$    **10** $8m \times 5$    **11** $n \times n$    **12** $y \times y$

**13** $6a \times a$    **14** $9f \times f$    **15** $q \times 7q$    **16** $3y \times 2y$

**17** $5b \times 3b$    **18** $8m \times 4p$    **19** $5a \times 9b$    **20** $10a \times 10a$

**21** $\dfrac{30m}{5}$    **22** $\dfrac{35x}{7}$    **23** $\dfrac{10a}{2}$    **24** $6n \times 3n$

**25** Luis says that $5m \times 4n \times 2p$ is equal to $40mnp$. Explain clearly whether Luis is correct.

**26** $\dfrac{2n}{n} = n$ or $\dfrac{2n}{n} = 2$? Which answer is correct?

**TASK M2.7**

In questions **1** to **9** answer 'true' or 'false'.

**1** $a + b = ab$    **2** $a + a = a^2$    **3** $5m + m = 6m$

**4** $6n^2 - n^2 = 6$    **5** $4y \times y = 4y^2$    **6** $7a \times 2b = 14ab$

**7** $16x \div 4 = 12x$    **8** $a \times 5 \times b = 5ab$    **9** $y \times y \times y = y^3$

Simplify

**10** $4a \times -6b$    **11** $-3m \times -2p$    **12** $-6a \div -3$

**13** $-15x \div 5$    **14** $-5a \times -2a$    **15** $-9f \times -4g$

**16** $-3p \times 7q$    **17** $8a \times -4c$    **18** $-a \times 3a$

**19** $-6y \times 11$    **20** $3b \times -6b$    **21** $-42a^2 \div -2$

In questions **22** to **30** copy and fill in the empty boxes.

**22** $5a \times \boxed{\phantom{x}} = 15ab$    **23** $9m \times \boxed{\phantom{x}} = 36m^2$    **24** $\dfrac{30n}{\boxed{\phantom{x}}} = 3n$

**25** $6\boxed{\phantom{x}} \times \boxed{\phantom{x}}y = 24xy$    **26** $\dfrac{\boxed{\phantom{x}}}{4} = 3b$    **27** $\boxed{\phantom{x}} \times -8y = -32y$

**28** $\dfrac{\boxed{\phantom{x}}}{7} = -6y$    **29** $\dfrac{-40n}{\boxed{\phantom{x}}} = 5n$    **30** $\boxed{\phantom{x}}p \times -9\boxed{\phantom{x}} = 45pq$

**31** Carlos writes $-8m \times -6n = 48mn$. Kate writes $-8m \times -6n = mn48$.
The teacher says that both answers are correct but one answer is written in a better way.
Which answer is this and why?

**1** Work out and write each answer as a number in index form.

**a** $5^3 \times 5^4$      **b** $6^4 \div 6^2$      **c** $3^8 \div 3^3$

**d** $9^4 \times 9^2$      **e** $2^7 \times 2$      **f** $4^9 \div 4$

**g** $2^3 \times 2^4 \times 2^2$      **h** $5^3 \times 5 \times 5^3$      **i** $5^6 \times 5^2 \div 5^4$

> **Remember:**
> $$a^m \times a^n = a^{m+n}$$
> $$a^m \div a^n = a^{m-n}$$

**2** Copy and complete.

**a** $2^6 \times 2 = \square$      **b** $3^4 \times \square = 3^9$      **c** $\square \times 6^3 = 6^7$

**d** $5^7 \div \square = 5^2$      **e** $8^{12} \div \square = 8^{11}$      **f** $\square \div 4^6 = 4^2$

**3** Answer true or false for each statement below.

**a** $2^4 \times 2 = 2^4$      **b** $4^2 \times 4^4 = 4^8$      **c** $7^8 \div 7^2 = 7^6$

**4** Work out and write each answer as a number in index form.

**a** $\dfrac{3^6 \times 3^4}{3^7}$      **b** $\dfrac{5^3 \times 5^2 \times 5^2}{5^5}$      **c** $\dfrac{9^7}{9^3 \times 9}$

**5** Explain why $3^2 \times 2^3$ is not equal to $6^5$.

**6** Which is larger?    $\boxed{\dfrac{3^5 \times 3^3}{3^4}}$   or   $\boxed{\dfrac{3^2 \times 3^6}{3^3}}$

**7** The volume of a carton is $2^7$ cm$^3$. How many cartons will fit into a box of volume $2^{12}$ cm$^3$?

**1** Work out and write each answer as a number in index form.

**a** $(4^2)^3$      **b** $(2^3)^3$      **c** $(7^4)^2$

**d** $(5^2)^4 \times 5^3$      **e** $(6^2) \times (6^2)^2$      **f** $\dfrac{(3^2)^5}{3^6}$

**g** $4^3 \times (4^3)^4$      **h** $\dfrac{(2^2)^6}{(2^3)^3}$      **i** $\dfrac{7^4 \times (7^3)^2}{7^5}$

> **Remember:**
> $$(a^m)^n = a^{mn}$$
> $$a^0 = 1$$

**2** What is the value of $8^0$?

**3** Simplify the expressions below.

a $x^4 \times x^3$      b $y^7 \times y^2$      c $a^6 \div a^2$

d $\dfrac{m^7}{m^3}$      e $(x^2)^4$      f $x^0$

g $(y^5)^3$      h $(a^0)^3$      i $(x^3)^2 \div x^2$

**4** Answer 'true' or 'false' for each statement below.

a $(x^4)^5 = x^9$      b $y^4 \times y^2 = y^8$      c $x^3 \times x = x^3$

d $\dfrac{n^6}{n} = n^5$      e $\dfrac{(x^3)^3}{(x^2)^3} = x^3$      f $\dfrac{(a^2)^4}{a} = a^6$

**5** Which rectangle has the larger area?

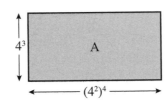
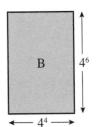

**6** Simplify the expressions below.

a $\dfrac{n^4 \times n^2}{n^5}$      b $\dfrac{(x^2)^2 \times x^5}{x^6}$      c $\dfrac{a \times (a^3)^3}{(a^3)^2}$

d $\dfrac{(x^2)^6 \times x^2}{(x^7)^2}$      e $\dfrac{m^9}{m^2 \times m^5}$      f $\dfrac{n^{10}}{(n^3)^2 \times n^2}$

g $\dfrac{(x^3)^4 \times (x^2)^5}{(x^3)^6}$      h $\dfrac{m^{19}}{(m^2)^4 \times (m^5)^2}$      i $\dfrac{(x^3)^3 \times (x^2)^5}{(x^6)^2 \times (x^2)^2}$

**7** Answer 'true' or 'false' for each statement below.

a $3x \times 3x = 9x^2$      b $5x^2 \times 4x^3 = 20x^6$      c $(3a^2)^2 = 9a^4$      d $\dfrac{15x^7}{3x^4} = 5x^3$

**8** Simplify the expressions below.

a $6n^5 \times n^4$      b $3m^4 \times 3m^4$      c $7n^6 \times 4n^2$

d $\dfrac{7m^6}{m^4}$      e $\dfrac{18n^7}{6n^3}$      f $\dfrac{10m^3 \times 3m^4}{2m^2}$

---

**TASK M2.9**                                      **Main Book Page 64**

Copy and complete.

**1** $3(a + 4) = \square + 12$            **2** $a(a + b) = a^2 + \square$

Multiply out

**3** $5(m + 2)$

**4** $4(x - 3)$

**5** $6(a - 8)$

**6** $2(3y + 5)$

**7** $9(2m - 4)$

**8** $3(x + y)$

**9** $6(2a - b)$

**10** $5(m + 3p)$

**11** $7(2x + 5)$

**12** $4(3p - 4q)$

**13** $a(b + c)$

**14** $x(x - y)$

**15** $m(m - 3p)$

**16** $c(2d + 1)$

**17** $2p(p + q)$

Write down and *simplify* an expression for the area of each shape below:

**18**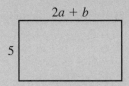
2a + b
5

**19**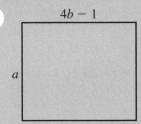
4b − 1
a

**20**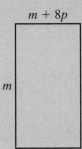
m + 8p
m

**21** Molly says that $m(m - n) = m^2 - mn$.
Show that this is true for $m = 6$ and $n = 4$.

**22** Austin and Gianna both simplify $4n(n + 2p)$.
Austin's answer: $4n^2 + 8np$
Gianna's answer: $4n^2 + 2p$
Who is correct? Explain why.

---

**TASK E2.4** ──────────────────────── **Main Book Page 65**

Copy and complete.

**1** $-4(x + 7) = \boxed{\phantom{x}} - 28$

**2** $-3(6b - 2) = -18b + \boxed{\phantom{x}}$

Expand

**3** $-3(a + 2)$

**4** $-6(b - 4)$

**5** $-5(x - 3)$

**6** $-2(3m - 4)$

**7** $-a(b - c)$

**8** $-m(2 - p)$

**9** $-y(x + z)$

**10** $-x(x + 3y)$

**11** $-(a - b)$

**12** $-(p + q)$

**13** $-b(2a - 3)$

**14** $-f(5g + 2h)$

**15** $-q(q - 8r)$

**16** $3a(3a + 4b)$

**17** $-8x(4x - 3y)$

In questions ⑱ to ㉓ copy and fill in the empty boxes.

**18** ☐$(m - 2) = -4m + 8$

**19** ☐$(n + 3) = -5n - 15$

**20** $-a(a$ ☐$) = -a^2 - 4a$

**21** $-p($ ☐$- 4q) = -p^2 + 4pq$

**22** ☐$(4m + 7n) = -12m^2 - 21mn$

**23** $-7y($ ☐$- 2p) = -14y^2 + 14py$

---

| **TASK M2.10** | **Main Book Page 65** |

Copy and complete.

**1** $3(4a + 7) - 5a =$ ☐$+ 21 - 5a =$ ☐$+ 21$

**2** $5(4x + 6) + 3(2x - 5) =$ ☐$+ 30 +$ ☐$- 15 =$ ☐$+ 15$

Simplify

**3** $3(a + 4) + 7$

**4** $6(m + 4) - 9$

**5** $5(x + 6) + 3x$

**6** $2(4y + 7) + 12$

**7** $9(2b + 4) + 4b$

**8** $7(5a + 6) - 10a$

Expand and simplify

**9** $3(x + 4) + 4(x + 2)$

**10** $2(4p + 3) + 5(p + 3)$

**11** $6(2m + 5) + 3(4m + 1)$

**12** $7(3a + 2) + 4(a - 2)$

**13** $3(8y + 6) + 2(2y - 5)$

**14** $5n + 9 + 6(2x + 3)$

**15** $4b + 9(3b + 6) - 24$

**16** $7(4c + 7) + 3(2c - 8)$

Write down an expression for each area shown below. Expand and simplify the answer where possible.

**17**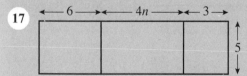

**18**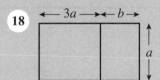

**19**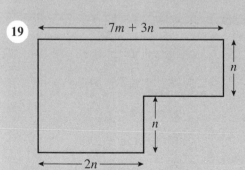

**20**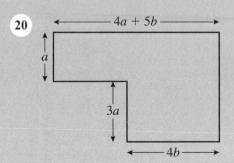

**TASK M2.11** ——————————————————————— **Main Book Page 67**

Copy and complete.

**1** $4a + 6 = 2(2a + \square)$ **2** $6a + 2 = 2(3a + \square)$ **3** $6m - 9 = 3(2m - \square)$

**4** $18b - 12 = 6(\square - 2)$ **5** $16y + 28 = 4(\square + \square)$ **6** $40x - 24 = 8(\square - \square)$

Factorise the expressions below:

**7** $6x + 10$ **8** $8a + 12$ **9** $10p - 40$

**10** $20y - 25$ **11** $12m + 9$ **12** $36b - 12$

**13** $9x + 6y$ **14** $16a + 12b$ **15** $24m - 20p$

**16** $45f + 35g$ **17** $21a - 15b$ **18** $30x - 50y$

**19** $8p + 6q - 10r$ **20** $15x - 30y - 20z$ **21** $35a - 21b + 49c$

**TASK M2.12** ——————————————————————— **Main Book Page 68**

Copy and complete.

**1** $ab + af = a(b + \square)$ **2** $xy - xz = x(\square - z)$

**3** $4mp - 10m = 2m(2p - \square)$ **4** $n^2 + 7n = n(n + \square)$

**5** $f^2 - 9f = f(\square - 9)$ **6** $4ab + 18bc = 2b(\square + \square)$

Factorise the expressions below:

**7** $xy + yz$ **8** $a^2 - 6a$ **9** $b^2 + 4b$

**10** $c^2 + 9c$ **11** $mp - pq$ **12** $3xy + 9xz$

**13** $10ab - 15ac$ **14** $18wz - 15wy$ **15** $12fg - 21f$

**16** $4a^2 - 6a$ **17** $5p^2 - 30pq$ **18** $18mp + 30m$

**19** $8pq - 20q^2$ **20** $16xyz - 28y^2$ **21** $33a^2 + 55abc$

**22** 3 students factorise $6m^2 - 12mn$. Their answers are below:

$m(6m - 12n)$    $6m(m - 2n)$    $2m(3m - 6n)$

All the answers are correct but which answer is factorised *completely*?
Give a reason for your answer.

Factorise completely

**23** $8x^2 + 12xy$ **24** $30mn - 24n^2$ **25** $20y^2 - 12xyz$

26

**1** Solve these equations:

    **a** $n + 3 = 8$      **b** $n + 8 = 15$      **c** $n - 3 = 6$      **d** $n - 7 = 9$

    **e** $n + 12 = 43$      **f** $x - 9 = 19$      **g** $x - 24 = 18$      **h** $x + 37 = 60$

    **i** $x + 26 = 41$      **j** $x - 38 = 14$      **k** $n - 49 = 28$      **l** $n + 58 = 73$

**2** Ian thinks of a number and then subtracts 14. If the answer is 25, what number did Ian think of?

**3** Solve

    **a** $6 \times n = 30$      **b** $6n = 24$      **c** $3n = 21$      **d** $n - 14 = 21$

    **e** $n \div 3 = 5$      **f** $\dfrac{n}{4} = 2$      **g** $\dfrac{x}{10} = 6$      **h** $\dfrac{x}{7} = 4$

    **i** $\dfrac{x}{5} = 8$      **j** $8x = 48$      **k** $x - 34 = 28$      **l** $9x = 54$

**4** Find the value of $x$ in this rectangle.

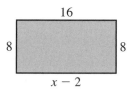

**5** Mel gets a maths test mark which is 7 times John's test mark. Mel scored 84%. What mark did John get?

**6** Solve

    **a** $x - 29 = 12$      **b** $4x = 28$      **c** $6 = \dfrac{x}{7}$      **d** $24 = x + 14$

    **e** $19 = x - 18$      **f** $36 = 9x$      **g** $48 = 6x$      **h** $9 = \dfrac{x}{9}$

**1** Solve these equations:

    **a** $n + 3 = 1$      **b** $n + 2 = 1$      **c** $n + 5 = 3$      **d** $n - 3 = -6$

    **e** $n + 8 = 0$      **f** $3n = -6$      **g** $10x = -8$      **h** $-5x = -20$

    **i** $4n = -28$      **j** $n \div 3 = -4$      **k** $\dfrac{x}{5} = -5$      **l** $\dfrac{x}{7} = -3$

**2** Pat thinks of a number and then adds 10. If the answer is 5, what number did Pat think of?

**3** Teresa doubles a number and gets the answer 9. What was the number?

**4** Solve

**a** $2x = 1$ **b** $2x = 5$ **c** $3n = 7$ **d** $5n = 4$

**e** $2n = -3$ **f** $5x = 7$ **g** $7x = -4$ **h** $3n = -11$

> **Remember:**
> if $3x = 2$ then
> $x = \dfrac{2}{3}$

**5** Sam trebles a recipe and needs 10 oranges. How many oranges were needed in the recipe?

**6** Solve these equations:

**a** $\dfrac{n}{4} = 5$ **b** $\dfrac{n}{-6} = 3$ **c** $n \div 5 = -4$ **d** $8 = \dfrac{n}{-6}$

**e** $5n = -3$ **f** $7 = \dfrac{n}{-2}$ **g** $9n = -7$ **h** $-5 = 6n$

**i** $2 = 7n$ **j** $1 = \dfrac{n}{-6}$ **k** $-8n = 5$ **l** $3 = -11n$

---

**TASK M2.14** ———————————————— **Main Book Page 72**

In questions **1** to **3** , copy and fill in the empty boxes.

**1** $\boxed{3n} + 2 = 20$

$\boxed{3n} = 18$

$n = \boxed{\phantom{0}}$

**2** $\boxed{5n} + 6 = 26$

$\boxed{5n} = \boxed{\phantom{0}}$

$n = \boxed{\phantom{0}}$

**3** $\boxed{4x} - 7 = 1$

$\boxed{4x} = \boxed{\phantom{0}}$

$x = \boxed{\phantom{0}}$

Solve these equations:

**4** $2n + 1 = 9$ **5** $3n + 8 = 17$ **6** $6n + 4 = 16$

**7** $3n + 5 = 20$ **8** $4x + 6 = 18$ **9** $5x - 2 = 18$

**10** $8x - 1 = 23$ **11** $6x - 7 = 23$ **12** $3n - 8 = 19$

**13** Find the value of $x$ in this rectangle.

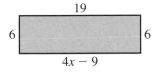

19

6 · · 6

$4x - 9$

Solve:

**14** $8x + 2 = 50$ **15** $55 = 9x - 8$ **16** $32 = 6n - 10$

**17** $62 = 6n + 8$ **18** $7x - 14 = 35$ **19** $39 = 3x + 9$

**20** $34 = 5x - 6$ **21** $8n - 26 = 30$ **22** $29 = 9x - 7$

**TASK E2.6** ———————————————— **Main Book Page 73**

In questions **1** to **3** , copy and fill in the empty boxes.

**1**  $\boxed{3n} + 4 = 6$

$\boxed{3n} = 2$

$n = \dfrac{2}{\boxed{\phantom{0}}}$

**2**  $\boxed{5n} + 6 = 9$

$\boxed{5n} = \boxed{\phantom{0}}$

$n = \dfrac{\boxed{\phantom{0}}}{\boxed{\phantom{0}}}$

**3**  $10 = 18 \boxed{+2n}$

$\boxed{\phantom{0}} = 2n$

$\boxed{\phantom{0}} = n$

Solve these equations:

**4**  $5n + 4 = 7$

**5**  $2x + 5 = 10$

**6**  $4x + 7 = 10$

**7**  $8x + 5 = 10$

**8**  $3n + 6 = 13$

**9**  $2n - 9 = 2$

**10**  $4n - 2 = 1$

**11**  $9x - 5 = 2$

**12**  $10x + 14 = 37$

**13**  If we multiply a number by 5 and then add 3, the answer is 4. What is the number?

**14**  If we multiply a number by 7 and then subtract 2, the answer is 3. What is the number?

Solve:

**15**  $6 = 3n + 8$

**16**  $4 = 5 + 6n$

**17**  $6x + 7 = 6$

**18**  $8 = 20 + 4x$

**19**  $15 = 27 + 3x$

**20**  $-5 = 8x - 2$

**21**  $-26 = 14 - 5x$

**22**  $-12 = 8 + 4n$

**23**  $6n + 1 = -4$

# NUMBER 2　　　　　　　　　　　　　　　　　　3

**TASK M3.1/M3.2** ———————————————— **Main Book Page 80**

**1**  Copy each shape below and shade in the given fraction.

**a**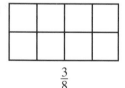

$\dfrac{3}{8}$

**b**

$\dfrac{3}{4}$

**c**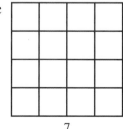

$\dfrac{7}{16}$

**d**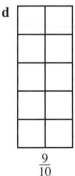

$\dfrac{9}{10}$

**2** Find $\frac{1}{10}$ of:     **a** 30       **b** 80       **c** 100       **d** 500

**3** Find $\frac{1}{7}$ of:     **a** 14       **b** 35       **c** 63       **d** 140

Work out:

**4** $\frac{1}{5}$ of 35       **5** $\frac{2}{3}$ of 18       **6** $\frac{3}{8}$ of 56       **7** $\frac{5}{7}$ of 42

**8** There are 30 students in a class. $\frac{2}{5}$ of them are girls. How many girls are there in the class?

**9** In a spelling test full marks were 54. How many marks did Simon get if he got $\frac{5}{6}$ of full marks?

**10** What fraction of each shape below is shaded?

  **a** 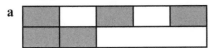       **b**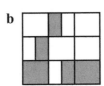

**11** Maddy has 12 pairs of shoes. 4 pairs of shoes are black.

  **a** What fraction of her shoes are black?

  **b** What fraction of her shoes are *not* black?

**12** In a food survey, 41 people were asked what their favourite meal was. 16 people choose 'pizza'.

  **a** What fraction of the people chose 'pizza'?

  **b** What fraction of the people did *not* choose 'pizza'?

**13** What fraction of the months of the year begin with the letter J?

**14** There are 60 minutes in 1 hour.
What fraction of 1 hour is:

  **a** 10 minutes       **b** 20 minutes

  **c** 45 minutes       **d** 50 minutes

  **e** 17 minutes       **f** 36 minutes

(Try and cancel your answers)

---

**TASK M3.3**            **Main Book Page 82**

Work out:

**1** $\frac{5}{7}$ of 63       **2** $\frac{5}{8}$ of 24       **3** $\frac{2}{9}$ of 72       **4** $\frac{3}{7}$ of 42

**5** $\frac{5}{9}$ of 27       **6** $\frac{7}{8}$ of 64       **7** $\frac{1}{6}$ of 126       **8** $\frac{9}{50}$ of 400

**9**  A toaster costs £25. In a sale, the price of a toaster is reduced by $\frac{2}{5}$.
How much does a toaster cost now?

**10**  A packet of biscuits contains 276 g. If a packet of biscuits now has $\frac{1}{3}$ extra, how much does it contain?

**11**  Some questions and answers are shown below. Which answer has no question matching it?

| $\frac{5}{8}$ of 48 | $\frac{2}{3}$ of 27 | 18 | 8 |

| $\frac{6}{7}$ of 42 | $\frac{7}{10}$ of 20 | 24 | 14 |

| | | 36 | 30 |

| $\frac{3}{5}$ of 45 | $\frac{2}{9}$ of 36 | 27 | |

**12**  In seven years, a footballer scored 216 goals and $\frac{2}{9}$ of these were headers.
How many headers did he score?

**13**  A box of 'Cleano' now contains $\frac{2}{3}$ extra. Normally it contains 420 g.
How much does it have now?

**14**  Robert takes £60 from the cashpoint. He spends $\frac{2}{5}$ of it on a meal and $\frac{1}{3}$ of it on a present for a friend. He spends $\frac{3}{8}$ of the remaining money on a T-shirt. How much does the T-shirt cost?

**15**  In a sale, a TV has $\frac{3}{7}$ knocked off the price. If it was originally priced at £392, what does it cost in the sale?

**16**  A large snowball has a volume of 750 cm³. After one hour its volume decreases by $\frac{3}{5}$.
This new volume decreases by $\frac{3}{5}$ during the next hour. Work out the volume of the snowball after 2 hours.

---

**TASK M3.4/M3.5** ———————————————————— **Main Book Page 84**

**1**  Which shapes have an equivalent fraction shaded?

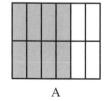

A

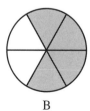

B

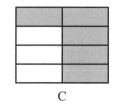

C

**2** Copy this rectangle.

Shade a fraction equivalent to $\frac{3}{5}$.

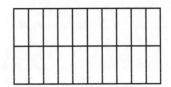

**3** Copy and complete these equivalent fractions by filling in the box.

**a** $\frac{3}{4} = \frac{\square}{20}$

**b** $\frac{1}{3} = \frac{\square}{12}$

**c** $\frac{5}{8} = \frac{10}{\square}$

**d** $\frac{2}{9} = \frac{\square}{36}$

**e** $\frac{3}{8} = \frac{15}{\square}$

**f** $\frac{7}{20} = \frac{35}{\square}$

**g** $\frac{4}{5} = \frac{\square}{30}$

**h** $\frac{5}{9} = \frac{45}{\square}$

**4** Cancel each fraction below to its lowest terms.

**a** $\frac{18}{20}$

**b** $\frac{12}{30}$

**c** $\frac{6}{15}$

**d** $\frac{24}{32}$

**e** $\frac{6}{18}$

**f** $\frac{25}{100}$

**g** $\frac{21}{28}$

**h** $\frac{32}{48}$

**i** $\frac{63}{81}$

**j** $\frac{88}{121}$

**5** Which of the fractions below are the same as $\frac{7}{8}$?

**a** $\frac{21}{24}$

**b** $\frac{16}{18}$

**c** $\frac{14}{24}$

**d** $\frac{35}{40}$

**e** $\frac{21}{27}$

**f** $\frac{56}{64}$

**6** Find the fractions in the table which are equivalent to $\frac{4}{9}$.

Rearrange the chosen letters to show a salad vegetable.

| $\frac{32}{72}$ | $\frac{40}{90}$ | $\frac{12}{20}$ | $\frac{45}{81}$ | $\frac{28}{63}$ | $\frac{20}{45}$ | $\frac{28}{56}$ | $\frac{12}{27}$ | $\frac{16}{45}$ | $\frac{24}{54}$ |
|---|---|---|---|---|---|---|---|---|---|
| D | H | B | U | S | A | M | R | Y | I |

---

**TASK M3.6** ———————————————————————— **Main Book Page 86**

**1** Copy and use the diagrams to

*explain* why $\frac{2}{3}$ is larger than $\frac{7}{12}$.

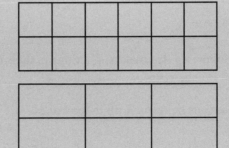

**2 a** $\dfrac{1}{2} = \dfrac{\square}{16}$   **b** Which is larger, $\dfrac{1}{2}$ or $\dfrac{9}{16}$?

**3** Write down each *smaller* fraction, explaining your reasons clearly.

  **a** $\dfrac{5}{8}$ or $\dfrac{3}{4}$   **b** $\dfrac{9}{10}$ or $\dfrac{26}{30}$   **c** $\dfrac{6}{7}$ or $\dfrac{7}{8}$

**4** Place in order, *largest first*:

  **a** $\dfrac{7}{20}, \dfrac{1}{4}, \dfrac{3}{10}$   **b** $\dfrac{11}{16}, \dfrac{5}{8}, \dfrac{19}{32}$   **c** $\dfrac{13}{18}, \dfrac{2}{3}, \dfrac{5}{9}$   **d** $\dfrac{1}{8}, \dfrac{5}{48}, \dfrac{1}{6}$

**5 a** $\dfrac{3}{8} = \dfrac{\square}{16}$   **b** $\dfrac{1}{2} = \dfrac{\square}{16}$   **c** Does $\dfrac{7}{16}$ lie between $\dfrac{3}{8}$ and $\dfrac{1}{2}$?

**6 a** $\dfrac{1}{4} = \dfrac{\square}{40}$   **b** $\dfrac{3}{10} = \dfrac{\square}{40}$   **c** Write down a fraction which lies between $\dfrac{1}{4}$ and $\dfrac{3}{10}$.

**7 a** $\dfrac{5}{7} = \dfrac{\square}{35}$   **b** $\dfrac{4}{5} = \dfrac{\square}{35}$   **c** Write down a fraction which lies between $\dfrac{5}{7}$ and $\dfrac{4}{5}$.

**8** For each pair of fractions below, write down a fraction which lies between them:

  **a** $\dfrac{4}{15}$ and $\dfrac{1}{3}$   **b** $\dfrac{5}{6}$ and $\dfrac{11}{12}$   **c** $\dfrac{7}{10}$ and $\dfrac{8}{10}$

---

**TASK M3.7**                                                                 **Main Book Page 88**

**1** Is $0{\cdot}027$ the same as $\dfrac{27}{1000}$?

**2** Is $0{\cdot}8$ the same as $\dfrac{4}{5}$?

**3** Is $0{\cdot}45$ the same as $\dfrac{7}{20}$?

**4** Change the following decimals to fractions in their most simple form.

  **a** $0{\cdot}03$     **b** $0{\cdot}82$     **c** $0{\cdot}4$     **d** $0{\cdot}052$     **e** $0{\cdot}15$

**5** Copy the questions below and fill in the boxes.

  **a** $\dfrac{11}{20} = \dfrac{\square}{100} = 0{\cdot}\square$     **b** $\dfrac{7}{200} = \dfrac{\square}{1000} = 0{\cdot}\square$

**6** Convert the fractions below to decimals.

    **a** $\dfrac{3}{20}$       **b** $\dfrac{19}{25}$       **c** $\dfrac{103}{200}$       **d** $\dfrac{3}{8}$       **e** $\dfrac{13}{25}$

**7** Freya thinks that $0.3$ is larger than $\dfrac{2}{5}$. Explain fully whether she is correct or not.

**8** Which is smaller $\boxed{\dfrac{7}{20}}$ or $\boxed{0.4}$ ?

    Explain your answer fully.

**9** Which number below is the odd one out?

    $\boxed{\dfrac{11}{25}}$     $\boxed{0.11}$     $\boxed{0.44}$     $\boxed{\dfrac{22}{50}}$

**10** Change the fractions below to decimals by dividing the numerator by the denominator.

    **a** $\dfrac{5}{9}$       **b** $\dfrac{1}{11}$       **c** $\dfrac{5}{12}$

---

**TASK M3.8**                   **Main Book Page 89**

**1** Which is larger?

    **a** $0.06$ or $0.5$       **b** $0.038$ or $0.04$       **c** $0.74$ or $0.742$

**2** $0.03 > 0.026$     Is this true or false?

**3** $0.6 < 0.546$     Is this true or false?

**4** Four people are asked to rate 4 different mobile phones. Each phone gets an average rating out of 10 as shown below:

| Phone A | 7·69 |
|---|---|

| Phone B | 6·9 |
|---|---|

| Phone C | 7·09 |
|---|---|

| Phone D | 7·7 |
|---|---|

    **a** Which phone has the highest rating?

    **b** Write down the phones in the order of the ratings, starting with the highest.

**5** Morgan says that $5.64$ is more than $5.628$. Explain clearly whether she is correct or not.

**6** For each set of numbers below, arrange the numbers in order of size, smallest first.

    **a** $0.03, 0.3, 0.003$          **b** $0.91, 0.902, 0.92, 0.091$

    **c** $0.073, 0.07, 0.75, 0.712$       **d** $0.418, 0.408, 0.48, 0.048$

    **e** $7.06, 7.1, 7.102, 7.07, 7.13$

**7** Five runners complete a race. Their times are shown below.

| Nathan | David | Deven | Brody | Luka |
|--------|-------|-------|-------|------|
| 48·27 s | 48·2 s | 49·01 s | 49·1 s | 48·18 s |

Write down the names of the quickest 3 runners in the order in which they finished the race.

**8** In the questions below, answer true or false.

a  0·08 is more than 0·7      b  0·603 is more than 0·068

c  0·36 is more than 0·308      d  0·4 is less than 0·38

e  0·027 is less than 0·03      f  0·056 is more than 0·07

**9** Arrange the numbers below in order of size, smallest first.

$$\frac{3}{20} \qquad \frac{1}{4} \qquad 0·2 \qquad 0·18 \qquad \frac{3}{25} \qquad 0·23$$

**TASK M3.9/M3.10** ———————————————— **Main Book Page 91**

Change the following improper fractions to mixed numbers.

**1**  $\frac{8}{3}$     **2** $\frac{7}{6}$     **3** $\frac{14}{5}$     **4** $\frac{8}{5} = 1\frac{\square}{5}$

**5** $\frac{7}{3} = \square\frac{\square}{3}$     **6** $\frac{17}{8} = 2\frac{\square}{8}$     **7** $\frac{9}{2}$     **8** $\frac{13}{3}$

**9** $\frac{19}{5}$     **10** $\frac{31}{4}$     **11** $\frac{23}{8}$     **12** $\frac{40}{9}$

Change the following mixed numbers to improper fractions.

**13** $1\frac{2}{5}$     **14** $2\frac{5}{8}$     **15** $3\frac{5}{6}$     **16** $3\frac{4}{5} = \frac{19}{\square}$

**17** $4\frac{2}{3} = \frac{\square}{3}$     **18** $5\frac{3}{4} = \frac{\square}{4}$     **19** $2\frac{7}{8}$     **20** $4\frac{5}{6}$

**21** $3\frac{1}{5}$     **22** $9\frac{3}{4}$     **23** $8\frac{2}{3}$     **24** $9\frac{3}{8}$

**25** Which is larger $5\frac{2}{3}$ or $\frac{19}{3}$ ?

Explain your answer fully.

In the questions below, change improper fractions to mixed numbers or mixed numbers to improper fractions.

**26** $\dfrac{47}{8}$  **27** $\dfrac{35}{4}$  **28** $\dfrac{26}{5}$  **29** $6\dfrac{2}{3}$  **30** $2\dfrac{1}{7}$  **31** $\dfrac{82}{9}$

**32** For each pair of numbers below, write down which number is larger.

   **a** $\dfrac{23}{7}$ or $3\dfrac{1}{7}$      **b** $4\dfrac{7}{9}$ or $\dfrac{44}{9}$      **c** $\dfrac{51}{8}$ or $6\cdot5$

---

**TASK M3.11**                                         **Main Book Page 93**

Work out

**1** $\dfrac{1}{4}+\dfrac{2}{4}$      **2** $\dfrac{8}{9}-\dfrac{7}{9}$      **3** $\dfrac{8}{11}-\dfrac{5}{11}$      **4** $\dfrac{7}{20}+\dfrac{4}{20}$

**5** Tim ate $\dfrac{3}{7}$ of his pizza and gave $\dfrac{2}{7}$ of his pizza to his sister who ate it straight away.

   What total fraction of the pizza has been eaten?

**6** Mr. Agg gave $\dfrac{4}{9}$ of his money to his son and $\dfrac{4}{9}$ of his money to his daughter.

   In total, what fraction of his money did he give away?

**7** Copy and complete:

   **a** $\dfrac{2}{7}+\dfrac{3}{8}$         **b** $\dfrac{5}{6}-\dfrac{1}{4}$         **c** $\dfrac{7}{10}-\dfrac{2}{9}$

   $=\dfrac{\square}{56}+\dfrac{\square}{56}$     $=\dfrac{\square}{12}-\dfrac{\square}{12}$     $=\dfrac{\square}{90}-\dfrac{\square}{\square}$

   $=\dfrac{\square}{56}$           $=\dfrac{\square}{\square}$          $=\dfrac{\square}{\square}$

In questions **8** to **9**, which answer is the odd one out?

**8** **a** $\dfrac{5}{6}-\dfrac{5}{12}$      **b** $\dfrac{1}{3}+\dfrac{1}{4}$      **c** $\dfrac{2}{3}-\dfrac{1}{12}$

**9** **a** $\dfrac{1}{4}+\dfrac{1}{16}$      **b** $\dfrac{11}{16}-\dfrac{3}{8}$      **c** $\dfrac{3}{16}+\dfrac{5}{8}$

Work out

**10** $\dfrac{2}{5}+\dfrac{4}{9}$    **11** $\dfrac{6}{7}-\dfrac{3}{5}$    **12** $\dfrac{5}{8}-\dfrac{1}{3}$    **13** $\dfrac{2}{5}+\dfrac{3}{10}$

**14** $\dfrac{4}{5}-\dfrac{2}{3}$    **15** $\dfrac{1}{4}+\dfrac{1}{6}$    **16** $\dfrac{9}{10}-\dfrac{1}{2}$    **17** $\dfrac{2}{11}+\dfrac{3}{10}$

**18** Tanya gives $\frac{1}{3}$ of her clothes to her sister and $\frac{1}{10}$ of her clothes to a cousin.

What fraction of her clothes did Tanya give away in total?

**19** In a class, $\frac{1}{4}$ of the students come by bus and $\frac{3}{5}$ of the students walk.

The rest of the students come by car. What fraction of the students come by car?

---

**TASK E3.1** ——————————————————— **Main Book Page 94**

**1** **a** Write $2\frac{3}{5}$ as an improper fraction.

**b** Work out $2\frac{3}{5} + \frac{3}{4}$, giving the answer as a mixed number.

**2** Work out

**a** $4\frac{1}{2} + 2\frac{2}{3}$      **b** $3\frac{3}{4} + 2\frac{3}{4}$      **c** $7\frac{3}{4} + \frac{7}{10}$      **d** $1\frac{3}{8} + 6\frac{1}{3}$

**3** I travel along the road from A to C.
What is the total distance I travel?

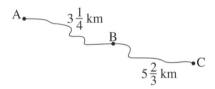

**4** Which answer is the odd one out?

**a** $3\frac{1}{6} - \frac{3}{4}$      **b** $3\frac{3}{10} - 1\frac{1}{3}$      **c** $4\frac{3}{4} - 2\frac{1}{3}$

**5** Joynul has a $1\frac{3}{4}$ metre length of wood.

He cuts off $1\frac{1}{10}$ metre of wood.

What length of wood has he got left?

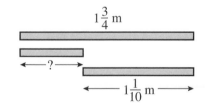

**6**

The number in each box opposite is found by adding the numbers in the 2 boxes below it.
Work backwards to find the two missing numbers.

Pyramid boxes: top box $4\frac{5}{12}$; middle row right box $2\frac{1}{6}$; bottom row boxes $1\frac{1}{2}$ and $\frac{2}{3}$.

**7** Ethan likes reading books. During one year $\frac{2}{5}$ of the books he reads are written by American authors. $\frac{1}{3}$ of the authors are British and $\frac{1}{10}$ are French. What fraction of the books he reads are not written by American, British or French authors?

**8** 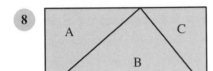 A rectanglar field has an area of 4 hectares. If area A is $1\frac{1}{2}$ hectares and area B is $1\frac{3}{5}$ hectares, work out the size of area C.

---

**TASK M3.12** | **Main Book Page 95**

Work out (cancel your answers where possible)

**1** $\frac{1}{2}$ of $\frac{1}{3}$

**2** $\frac{1}{3}$ of $\frac{1}{5}$

**3** $\frac{3}{4}$ of $\frac{1}{2}$

**4** $\frac{2}{3}$ of $\frac{3}{5}$

**5** $\frac{1}{4} \times \frac{1}{8}$

**6** $\frac{1}{7} \times \frac{1}{6}$

**7** $\frac{1}{4} \times \frac{2}{7}$

**8** $\frac{3}{5} \times \frac{2}{9}$

**9** $\frac{3}{4} \times 6$

**10** $\frac{5}{6} \times 4$

**11** $\frac{5}{8} \times 10$

**12** $\frac{2}{3} \times 6$

**13** Tony runs for $\frac{5}{12}$ of an hour.

Davina runs for $\frac{6}{15}$ of an hour.

Who runs for longer and by how much longer (Give your answer in minutes)?

**14** $\frac{1}{4}$ of Sarah's sweets are strawberry flavoured. She eats $\frac{5}{6}$ of these strawberry sweets.

What fraction of all of her sweets has she now eaten?

**15** Which question below gives a different answer?

A | $\frac{3}{5} \times 50$    B | $\frac{5}{8} \times 40$    C | $\frac{5}{6} \times 36$

**16** Callum has half a pizza.
Andrea has one sixth of a pizza.
Alex has one third of a pizza.

During the next 5 minutes, Callum eats $\frac{5}{6}$ of his remaining pizza, Andrea eats $\frac{1}{2}$ of her remaining pizza and Alex eats $\frac{3}{4}$ of his remaining pizza.

Who eats the most pizza during this 5 minutes?

38

**1** Copy and complete

$$\frac{2}{3} \times 2\frac{1}{5} = \frac{2}{3} \times \frac{\square}{5} = \frac{\square}{15} = \square\frac{\square}{15}$$

**2** Copy and complete

$$3\frac{1}{2} \times 4\frac{1}{3} = \frac{\square}{2} \times \frac{\square}{3} = \frac{\square}{6} = \square\frac{\square}{6}$$

**3** Match each question below to its correct answer. One answer is an odd one out.

| A | $1\frac{4}{5} \times 3\frac{1}{2}$ |
|---|---|

| B | $2\frac{2}{3} \times 1\frac{3}{7}$ |
|---|---|

| C | $4\frac{1}{2} \times 1\frac{7}{10}$ |
|---|---|

$7\frac{13}{20}$    $6\frac{3}{10}$

$6\frac{2}{3}$    $3\frac{17}{21}$

**4** Find the area of each of the 3 rooms below:

**a**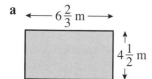
$6\frac{2}{3}$ m ,  $4\frac{1}{2}$ m

**b**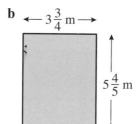
$3\frac{3}{4}$ m ,  $5\frac{4}{5}$ m

**c**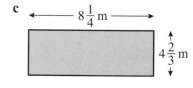
$8\frac{1}{4}$ m ,  $4\frac{2}{3}$ m

**5** Work out

**a** $\frac{1}{4} - \left(\frac{1}{4} \times \frac{1}{4}\right)$

**b** $\frac{1}{3} + \left(\frac{1}{3} \times \frac{1}{3}\right) + \left(\frac{1}{3} \times \frac{1}{3} \times \frac{1}{3}\right)$

**6** Work out $\left(2\frac{1}{2} \times \frac{5}{6}\right) - \left(\frac{2}{3} \times 1\frac{3}{4}\right)$

**7** Find the value of $n$ if $n \div 2\frac{3}{4} = 1\frac{3}{5}$

**1** Copy and complete

$$\frac{1}{7} \div \frac{1}{3} = \frac{1}{7} \times \frac{\square}{1} = \frac{\square}{7}$$

**2** Copy and complete

$$\frac{4}{9} \div \frac{3}{5} = \frac{4}{9} \times \frac{\square}{3} = \frac{\square}{\square}$$

Work out

**3** $10 \div \frac{1}{2}$

**4** $6 \div \frac{1}{3}$

**5** $\frac{1}{7} \div \frac{1}{4}$

**6** $\frac{1}{2} \div \frac{1}{3}$

**7** $\frac{2}{9} \div \frac{1}{4}$

**8** $\frac{3}{7} \div \frac{2}{3}$

**9** $\frac{2}{11} \div \frac{8}{9}$

**10** $\frac{9}{10} \div \frac{3}{4}$

**11** How many whole rods of length $\frac{3}{16}$ m can be cut from a pole of length $\frac{9}{10}$ m?

**12** Which question below gives a different answer?

| A | $\frac{4}{7} \div \frac{2}{3}$ |
|---|---|

| B | $\frac{7}{10} \div \frac{3}{4}$ |
|---|---|

| C | $\frac{2}{3} \div \frac{5}{7}$ |
|---|---|

**13** Carl is a fitness instructor. Each lesson he gives lasts for $\frac{2}{3}$ of a hour.

If he worked for 22 hours during one week, how many lessons did he teach?

**14** Which question below gives the larger answer and by how much?

$$\frac{3}{8} \div \frac{2}{3}$$     $$\frac{1}{4} \div \frac{4}{7}$$

**15** How many $\frac{3}{4}$ metre pieces of wood are needed to cover a 6 metre strip if the pieces of wood are laid end to end?

---

**TASK E3.3** ——————————————— **Main Book Page 98**

**1** Copy and complete

$$2\frac{1}{4} \div \frac{3}{5} = \frac{\square}{4} \div \frac{3}{5} = \frac{\square}{4} \times \frac{\square}{3} = \frac{\square}{12} = \frac{\square}{4} = 3\frac{\square}{4}$$

**2** Copy and complete

$$1\frac{1}{2} \div 1\frac{1}{6} = \frac{\square}{2} \div \frac{\square}{6} = \frac{\square}{2} \times \frac{6}{\square} = \frac{\square}{\square} = \frac{\square}{7} = \square\frac{\square}{7}$$

Work out

**3** $3\frac{1}{2} \div \frac{4}{5}$

**4** $1\frac{3}{4} \div \frac{2}{3}$

**5** $2\frac{3}{5} \div 1\frac{1}{6}$

**6** $3\frac{2}{3} \div 1\frac{3}{8}$

**7** Match each question to the correct answer (one answer is the odd one out):

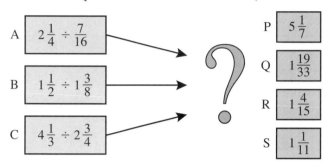

A $\quad 2\frac{1}{4} \div \frac{7}{16}$

B $\quad 1\frac{1}{2} \div 1\frac{3}{8}$

C $\quad 4\frac{1}{3} \div 2\frac{3}{4}$

P $\quad 5\frac{1}{7}$

Q $\quad 1\frac{19}{33}$

R $\quad 1\frac{4}{15}$

S $\quad 1\frac{1}{11}$

**8** Zoe has $42\frac{3}{4}$ kg of flour to pack into $1\frac{1}{2}$ kg bags. How many complete bags can she make up?

**9** Work out

**a** $1\frac{3}{4} + \left(1\frac{1}{3} \times 1\frac{1}{4}\right)$ $\qquad$ **b** $3\frac{3}{4} - \left(2\frac{1}{5} \times 1\frac{1}{2}\right)$

**10** A TV comedy episode lasts for $\frac{5}{12}$ of an hour. George wants to watch as many episodes as possible back to back for 3 hours. How many complete episodes can he watch?

---

**TASK E3.4** $\qquad\qquad\qquad\qquad\qquad\qquad\qquad\qquad\qquad$ **Main Book Page 99**

> The reciprocal of a number is $\frac{1}{n}$ where $n$ can never equal zero. $n$ multiplied by the reciprocal of $n$ always equals 1.

**1** Choose the correct box for each sentence below:

**a** The reciprocal of 3 is $\quad\boxed{1}\quad\boxed{\dfrac{1}{3}}\quad\boxed{\dfrac{3}{10}}$

**b** The reciprocal of 10 is $\quad\boxed{0\cdot1}\quad\boxed{1}\quad\boxed{\dfrac{5}{10}}$

**c** The reciprocal of 4 is $\quad\boxed{\dfrac{4}{10}}\quad\boxed{0\cdot25}\quad\boxed{1}$

**2** $0\cdot4 \times 2\cdot5 = 1$ and $0\cdot4 \times 3 = 1\cdot2$
Write down the reciprocal of $0\cdot4$

**3** Write down the reciprocal of each number below:

**a** 7 $\qquad$ **b** 9 $\qquad$ **c** $\dfrac{1}{5}$ $\qquad$ **d** 20 $\qquad$ **e** $\dfrac{1}{6}$ $\qquad$ **f** 0.01

**4** If $\dfrac{3}{5} \times \dfrac{5}{3} = 1$, write down the reciprocal of $\dfrac{5}{3}$.

**5** If $\frac{2}{9} \times \frac{9}{2} = 1$, write down the reciprocal of $\frac{2}{9}$.

**6** If $\frac{8}{11} \times \frac{11}{8} = 1$, write down the reciprocal of $\frac{8}{11}$.

**7** Write down the reciprocal of:

 **a** $\frac{3}{4}$  **b** $\frac{7}{10}$  **c** $\frac{4}{19}$  **d** $3\frac{1}{2}$  **e** $\frac{m}{n}$

**8** Write down the reciprocal of the number $n$.

**9** What number needs to be multiplied by $\frac{1}{12}$ to give an answer of 1?

**10** Pair off the numbers below which are reciprocals of each other.

| 2 | 15 | 0·5 | $\frac{2}{3}$ | $\frac{1}{15}$ | $\frac{3}{2}$ |

# GEOMETRY 1     4

**TASK M4.1**     **Main Book Page 107**

**1** For each of these angles say whether they are acute, obtuse or reflex:

**a** 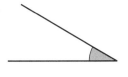  **b**   **c** 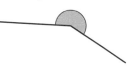  **d**

**e**   **f** 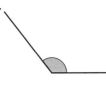  **g** 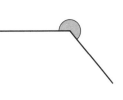  **h**

**i**   **j**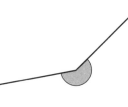

**2** Copy and complete the sentences below:
  **a** An acute angle is less than _____.
  **b** An obtuse angle is more than _____ and less than _____.
  **c** A reflex angle is more than _____.

**3** Which of the angles below are obtuse?
  187°    45°    120°    193°    243°    138°    31°

**4** Draw a triangle where all the angles are acute.

**5** Can you draw a triangle which has two obtuse angles inside it?

**6**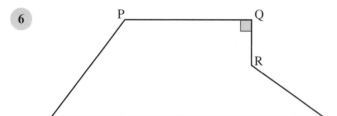
  **a** Is PQ̂R an acute angle?
  **b** Name a reflex angle inside this shape.
  **c** Name an obtuse angle inside this shape.
  **d** Name an acute angle inside this shape.
  **e** Give the name of the shape PQRST.

**7** How many obtuse angles can you see in this trapezium?

**8** **a** Is QR̂S acute or obtuse?
  **b** Is SP̂Q acute or obtuse?

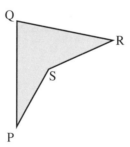

**9** Name the marked angles below:
  **a** 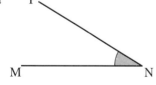    **b** 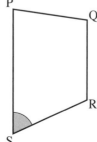    **c**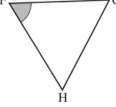

**TASK M4.2** ——————————————————————— **Main Book Page 108**

Find the angles marked with the letters.

**1**
$a$ 30°

**2**
$b$ 117°

**3**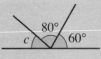
80° $c$ 60°

**4**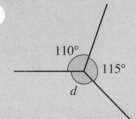
110° 115° $d$

**5**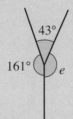
43° 161° $e$

**6**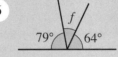
$f$ 79° 64°

**7**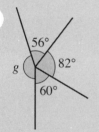
56° $g$ 82° 60°

**8**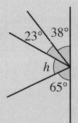
23° 38° $h$ 65°

**9**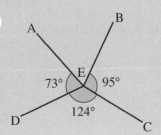
A B E D 73° 95° 124° C

**a** Work out the value of AÊB.
**b** Give a reason for your answer.

**10**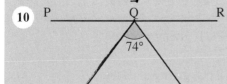
P Q R T 74° S

PQ̂T is equal to RQ̂S.
**a** Work out the value of PQ̂T.
**b** Give a reason for your answer.

44

**1** **a** Draw 2 perpendicular lines.

  **b** How large is the angle between the 2 perpendicular lines?

**2** Draw a triangle which has 2 sides which are perpendicular to each other.

In the questions below, find the angles marked with the letters.

**3**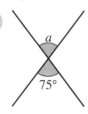

**4**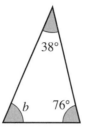

**5**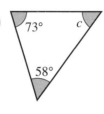

**6**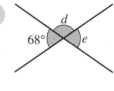

**7**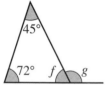

**8**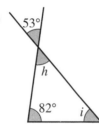

**9**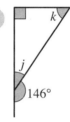

**10**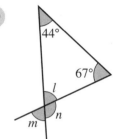

**11**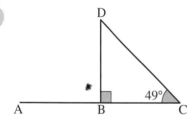

**a** Work out the value of $A\hat{B}D$, giving a reason for your answer.

**b** Work out the value of $B\hat{D}C$, giving a reason for your answer.

**12**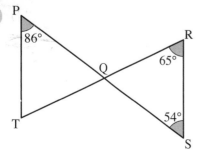

**a** Find the value of $R\hat{Q}S$, giving a reason for your answer.

**b** Find the value of $P\hat{Q}T$, giving a reason for your answer.

**c** Find the value of $P\hat{T}Q$, giving a reason for your answer.

Find the angles marked with the letters.

**1**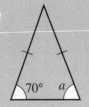

**2**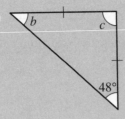

**3**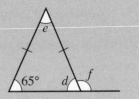

**4**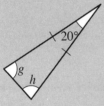

**5**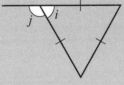

**6**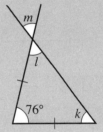

**7**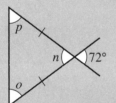

**8**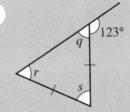

**9**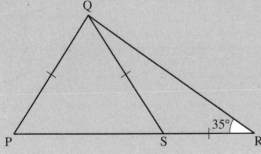

PQ = QS = SR

**a** Find the value of QŜR.
Give reasons for your answer.

**b** Find the value of PQ̂S.
Give reasons for your answer.

**10**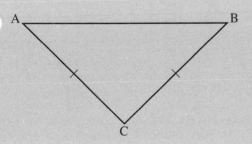

Triangle ABC is isosceles.
AĈB is obtuse.
Write down a possible value for AB̂C.
Give reasons for your answer.

46

**11** Triangle PQR is isosceles where PQ is equal to QR. $Q\hat{P}R = 38°$.
Work out the values of $P\hat{R}Q$ and $P\hat{Q}R$.

**12** Work out the value of $B\hat{A}D$
in the diagram opposite.
Give reasons for your answer.

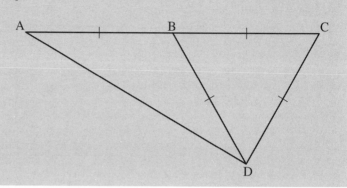

---

**TASK M4.5** ———————————————————————— **Main Book Page 112**

Find the angles marked with the letters.

**1**
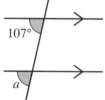
107°
$a$

**2**
$b$
39°

**3**
47°
$c$
$d$
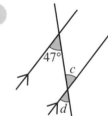

**4**
110°
$e$
$f$
$g$

**5**
124°
$h$  $k$
$i$  $j$
143°
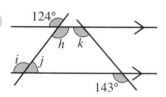

**6**
$l$
54°
86°
$n$
$m$
$o$
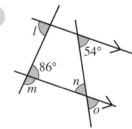

**7**
$s$
$p$
115°
$r$
$q$

**8**
30°
$t$
$u$
86°
$v$
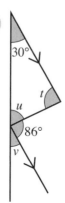

**9**

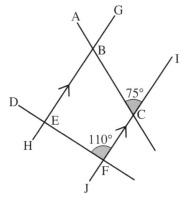

Lines AE and BD are parallel.
Write down the names of any 2 angles
which are corresponding.

**10**

Lines GH and IJ are parallel.

**a** Find the value of DÊB,
giving a reason for your answer.

**b** Find the value of CB̂E,
giving a reason for your answer.

**c** Find the value of DÊH,
giving a reason for your answer.

**11** Draw a diagram to show two angles which are alternate and equal.
Label the two angles and write down the names of these two equal angles (e.g. AB̂C = …).

**12** Is line PR parallel
to line SU?
Give reasons for
your answer.

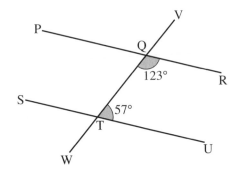

---

| **TASK M4.6/M4.7** | **Main Book Page 113** |

**1** Each of these shapes have a line of symmetry.
Copy them into your book and draw on a dotted line to show the *line of symmetry*:

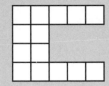
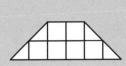

**2** Copy the patterns below on squared paper. Shade in as many squares as necessary to complete the symmetrical patterns. The dotted lines are lines of symmetry.

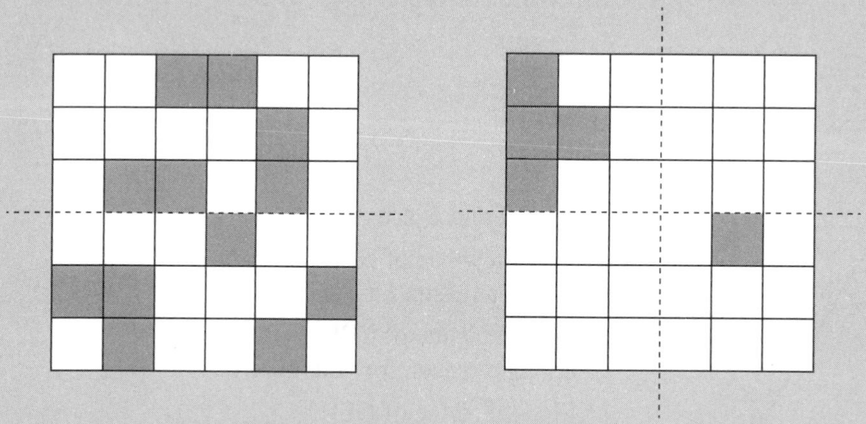

**3** Sketch these shapes in your book and draw on *all* the *lines of symmetry*.

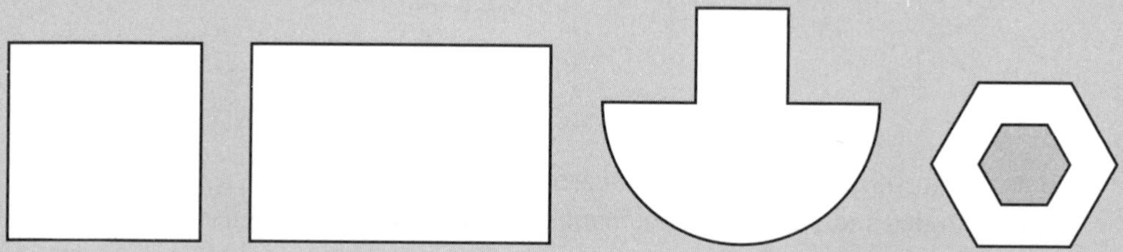

For each shape write the *order* of *rotational symmetry* (you may use tracing paper).

**4**

**5**

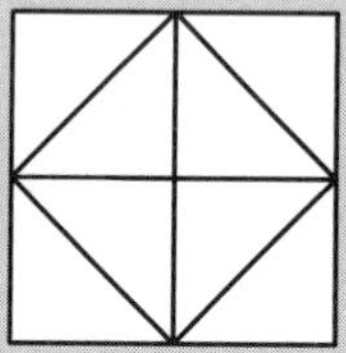

**6**

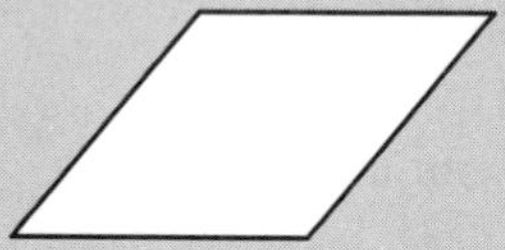

**7**

**8**

**9**

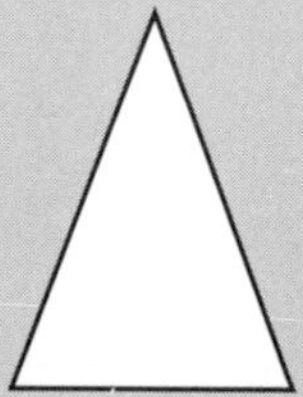

**10**

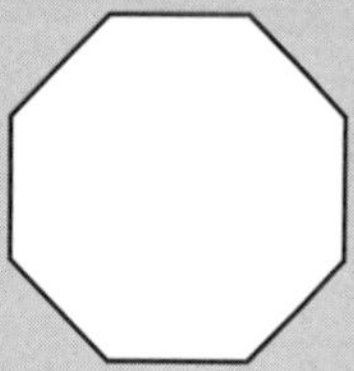

**11**

**12** Draw your own shape which has an order of rotational symmetry of 3.

**13** Draw a triangle which has *no* rotational symmetry.

**TASK M4.8** ─────────────────────────── **Main Book Page 115**

**1** Draw a parallelogram.

**2** How many lines of symmetry does a parallelogram have?

**3** Draw a quadrilateral which has two lines of symmetry *only*.

**4** Name this shape:

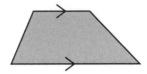

**5** Draw a rhombus in your book.
Draw in the two *diagonals*.
At the point of intersection of the two diagonals,
write down the angle between the diagonals.

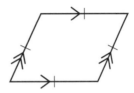

**6** Draw a quadrilateral which has no lines of symmetry.

**7** Copy and complete the two sentences below:

A parallelogram has two pairs of e _ _ _ _ opposite sides and two

pairs of p _ _ _ _ _ _ _ opposite sides. The diagonals cut each other

in h _ _ _.

**8** What is the *order* of rotational symmetry of a kite?

**TASK M4.9** ─────────────────────────── **Main Book Page 119**

Find the angles marked with letters.

**1**

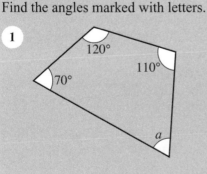

**2**

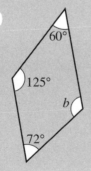

**3**

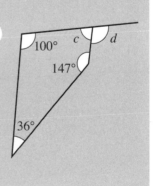

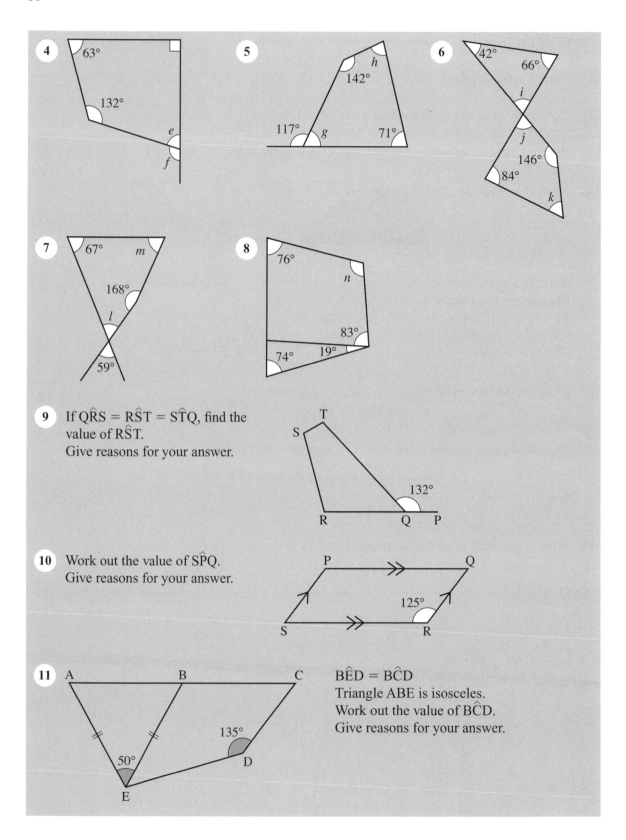

**4** 63° 132° e f

**5** h 142° 117° g 71°

**6** 42° 66° i j 146° 84° k

**7** 67° m 168° l 59°

**8** 76° n 83° 74° 19°

**9** If QR̂S = RŜT = ST̂Q, find the value of RŜT.
Give reasons for your answer.

T
S
132°
R    Q    P

**10** Work out the value of SP̂Q.
Give reasons for your answer.

P            Q
125°
S            R

**11** A            B            C
135°
D
50°
E

BÊD = BĈD
Triangle ABE is isosceles.
Work out the value of BĈD.
Give reasons for your answer.

**12**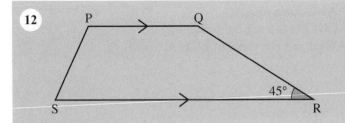

PQRS is a trapezium.
PŜR is 35° more than QR̂S.
Write down the values of each
angle in the trapezium.

---

**TASK M4.10** —————————————————— **Main Book Page 121**

**1** Copy and complete the sentence:
'The exterior angles of a polygon add up to _____.'

**2** An octagon has 8 sides. Find the size of each exterior angle of a *regular* octagon.

**3** A decagon has 10 sides.
  **a** Find the size of each exterior angle of a *regular* decagon.
  **b** Find the size of each interior angle of a *regular* decagon.

**4** Find the size of angle *a*.

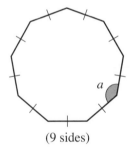

(9 sides)

**5** Find the exterior angles of *regular* polygons with
  **a** 18 sides    **b** 24 sides    **c** 45 sides

**6** Find the interior angle of each polygon in question **5** .

**7** The exterior angle of a *regular*
polygon is 24°. How many sides
has the polygon?

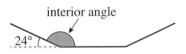

interior angle

24°

**8** The interior angle of a *regular* polygon is 162°.
How many sides has the polygon?

52

**9**

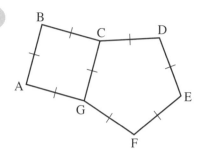

ABCG is a square.
CDEFG is a regular pentagon.
Work out the value of BĈD.

---

**1** Copy and complete below.
A pentagon can be split into _____ triangles.
Sum of interior angles = _____ × 180°
= _____°

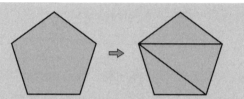

**2** Find the sum of the interior angles of an octagon.

**3** Find the sum of the interior angles of a polygon with 15 sides.

**4** Copy and complete below.
This polygon can be split into _____ triangles.
Sum of interior angles = _____ × 180° = _____
Add up all the given angles:
126° + 143° + 109° + 94° + 165° = _____°
angle x = _____°

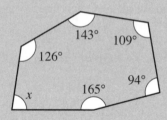

In the questions below, find the angles marked with letters.

**5**

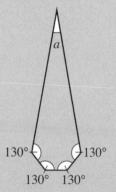

**6**

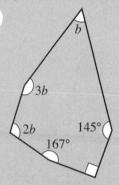

**7**

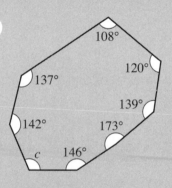

**8** Nine of the ten interior angles of a decagon each equal 145°.
Find the size of the other interior angle.

**9** All the angles in a polygon are measured as 156°, 145°, 135°, 82°, 165°, 75°, 152° and 178°.
The last angle is measured incorrectly. By how many degrees is it in error?

**TASK M4.11** ———————————————— **Main Book Page 125**

Use tracing paper if needed.

**1** Which shapes are *congruent* to shape A?

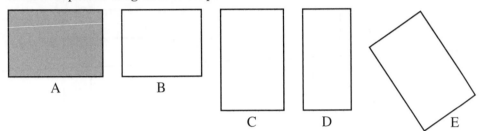

**2** Which shapes are congruent to shape P?

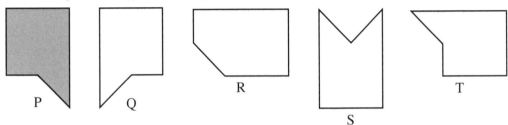

**3** Which 2 shapes are congruent?

**4** Which shapes are congruent to:
   **a** shape A    **b** shape B
   **c** shape E    **d** shape F

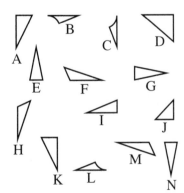

54

**5**

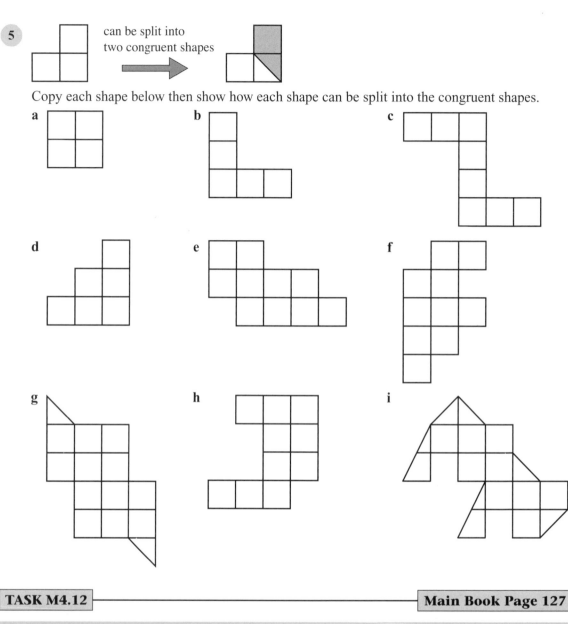

can be split into
two congruent shapes

Copy each shape below then show how each shape can be split into the congruent shapes.

a

b

c

d

e

f

g

h

i

**TASK M4.12** ———————————————————————— **Main Book Page 127**

**1**

**a** Use this grid to spell out this message.
(4, 1) (3, 4) (1, 3) (4, 5)
(1, 1) (3, 4)
(4, 2) (2, 2) (1, 5)

**b** Use co-ordinates to write
the word SENSIBLE.

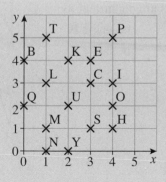

**2** Draw a horizontal axis from 0 to 16.
Draw a vertical axis from 0 to 16.
Plot the points below and join them with a ruler in the order given.

| | | | | | | | |
|---|---|---|---|---|---|---|---|
| (4, 9) | (1, 11) | (3, 8) | (1, 5) | (4, 7) | (6, 5) | (7, 5) | (8, 3) |
| (9, 5) | (11, 5) | (12, 7) | (15, 9) | (15, 10) | (12, 11) | (9, 11) | (8, 14) |
| (7, 11) | (6, 11) | (4, 9) | | | | | |

On the same picture plot the points below and join them up with a ruler in the order given.
Do not join the last point in the box above with the first point in the new box.

(15, 12)   (16, 12)   (16, 13)   (15, 13)   (15, 12)

(14, 14)   (13, 14)   (13, 15)   (14, 15)   (14, 14)

(12, 8)   (13, 8)

Draw a • at (13, 10)   Colour in the shape?

**TASK E4.2** ———————————————— **Main Book Page 129**

**1** Draw a horizontal axis from −5 to 12.
Draw a vertical axis from −5 to 12.
Plot the points below and join them with a ruler in the order given.

(0, −4)   (1, 1)   (1, −2)   (2, −3)   (1, −3)   (0, −4)

On the same  picture plot the points below and join them up with a ruler in the order given.
Do not join the last point in the box above with the first point in the new box.

(3, 6)   (3, 3)   (5, 5)   (6, 7)   (6, 10)

(−3, 9)   (−4, 9)   (−4, 10)   (−3, 10)

| | | | | | | |
|---|---|---|---|---|---|---|
| (7, −4) | (6, −3) | (5, −3) | (5, −1) | (4, 1) | (3, 2) | (2, 5) |
| (3, 6) | (4, 8) | (6, 10) | (5, 12) | (3, 12) | (2, 11) | (−1, 11) |
| (−3, 10) | (−3, 9) | (−2, 8) | (0, 8) | (1, 7) | (−1, 2) | (−1, −3) |
| (−2, −3) | (−3, −4) | (7, −4) | | | | |

(2, 11)   (2, 10)     (0, 8)   (1, 8)   Colour me in?

**2** Draw a horizontal axis from $-10$ to 8.

Draw a vertical axis from $-10$ to 8.

Plot the points below and join them with a ruler in the order given.

| | | | | | | |
|---|---|---|---|---|---|---|
| $(-10, -7)$ | $(-9, -6)$ | $(-8, -4)$ | $(-6, -2)$ | $(-4, -2)$ | $(-2, -1)$ | $(2, -1)$ |
| $(3, 1)$ | $(2, 2)$ | $(2, 4)$ | $(4, 2)$ | $(5, 2)$ | $(7, 4)$ | $(7, 2)$ |
| $(6, 1)$ | $(7, 0)$ | $(7, -1)$ | $(6, -1)$ | $(5, -2)$ | $(4, -1)$ | $(3, -1)$ |

On the same picture plot the points below and join them up with a ruler in the order given.
Do not join the last point in the box above with the first point in the new box.

| | | | | | | | |
|---|---|---|---|---|---|---|---|
| $(6, -1)$ | $(6, -3)$ | $(4, -5)$ | $(4, -9)$ | $(5, -9)$ | $(5, -4)$ | $(3, -6)$ | $(3, -9)$ |
| $(2, -9)$ | $(2, -6)$ | $(1, -5)$ | $(-1, -5)$ | $(-1, -3\frac{1}{2})$ | $(-1, -6)$ | $(-2, -7)$ | |
| $(-2, -9)$ | $(-3, -9)$ | $(-3, -6)$ | $(-4, -4)$ | $(-4, -6)$ | $(-5, -7)$ | $(-5, -9)$ | |
| $(-4, -9)$ | $(-4, -7)$ | $(-3, -6)$ | $(-4, -4)$ | $(-4, -3)$ | $(-7, -8)$ | $(-9, -8)$ | $(-10, -7)$ |

Colour me in?

---

**TASK M4.13** ———————————————————————————— **Main Book Page 131**

**1** Use translation vectors to describe the following translations.

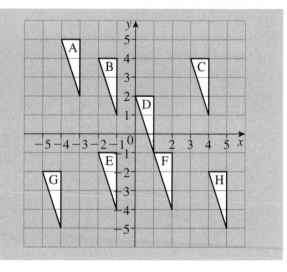

| | |
|---|---|
| **a** D to C | **b** E to D |
| **c** A to B | **d** E to F |
| **e** D to H | **f** H to F |
| **g** E to B | **h** E to G |
| **i** G to D | **j** F to C |

**2** Copy the grid opposite and draw shape A as shown. Translate shape A by each of the translation vectors shown below:

a $\begin{pmatrix} -4 \\ 1 \end{pmatrix}$ Label new shape B.

b $\begin{pmatrix} 1 \\ -3 \end{pmatrix}$ Label new shape C.

c $\begin{pmatrix} -4 \\ -3 \end{pmatrix}$ Label new shape D.

d $\begin{pmatrix} -1 \\ -5 \end{pmatrix}$ Label new shape E.

e Use a translation vector to describe the translation that moves shape D to E.

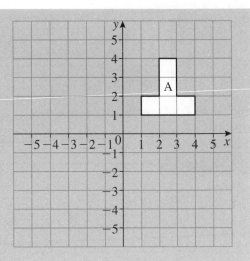

**TASK M4.14** ——————————————————— **Main Book Page 133**

Draw each shape below and reflect in the mirror line.

1

2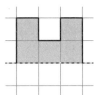

3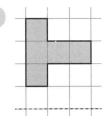

4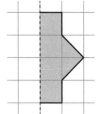

5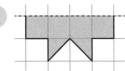

6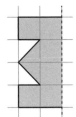

7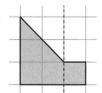

8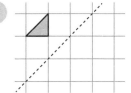

9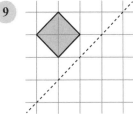

**10**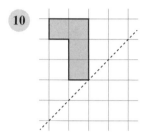

**11**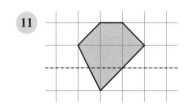

**12**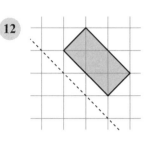

| TASK M4.15 | Main Book Page 135 |

**1**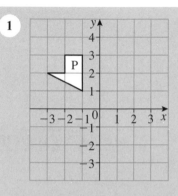

Copy the grid and shape opposite.

**a** Reflect shape P in the *x*-axis.
Label the image (new shape) Q.

**b** Reflect shape P in the *y*-axis.
Label the image (new shape) R.

**c** Reflect shape R in the *x*-axis.
Label the image S.

**d** Describe how you could transform
shape S into shape Q.

**2**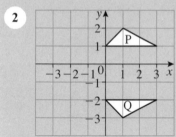

Kaylee reflects triangle P in the *x*-axis.
Explain clearly what she has done wrong.

**3** A point is reflected in the *y*-axis. Does the *y*-coordinate of the point stay the same?
Explain why you think this?

**4** Copy the diagram opposite then draw on
the line of reflection (mirror line) for

**a** shape A reflected onto shape B

**b** shape C reflected onto shape D

**c** shape E reflected onto shape F.

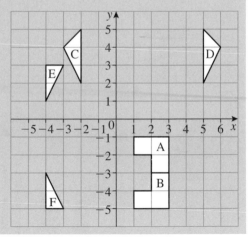

Use tracing paper.
For each question, draw the shape and the centre of rotation (C).
Rotate the shape as indicated and draw the image.

**1**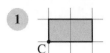

90° clockwise

**2**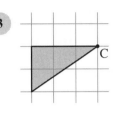

90° anticlockwise

**3**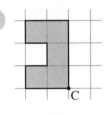

90° anticlockwise

**4**

180°

**5**

90° clockwise

**6**

90° anticlockwise

**7**

180°

**8**

90° anticlockwise

**9**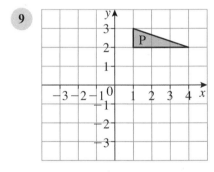

a Copy the diagram opposite.

b Rotate triangle P 90° clockwise about (0, 1).
  Label the image Q.

c Rotate triangle P 90° clockwise about (0, 2).
  Label the image R.

d Comment on the position of the image when
  a different centre of rotation is used.

**10** a Draw the x axis from −6 to 5.
  Draw the y-axis from −6 to 7.
  Draw rectangle A with vertices at (2, −2) (3, −2) (3, −5) (2, −5).

b Rotate rectangle A 90° clockwise about (2, −1). Label the image B.

c Rotate rectangle B 90° clockwise about (−2, −2). Label the image C.

d Rotate rectangle C 90° clockwise about the origin. Label the image D.

e Rotate rectangle D 90° clockwise about (−2, 2). Label the image E.

f Rotate rectangle E 90° clockwise about (3, 2). Label the image F.

g Describe *fully* the rotation which transforms rectangle A onto rectangle F.

60

**1**  Look at each of the following pairs of diagrams and decide whether or not one diagram is an enlargement of the other. For each part, write the scale factor of the enlargement or write 'not an enlargement'.

**a**

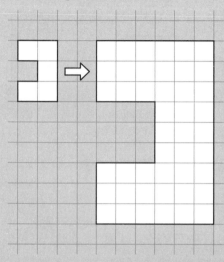

**b**

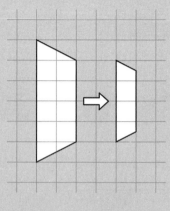

For questions **2** to **4** , copy the diagram and then draw an enlargement using the scale factor and centre of enlargement (C) given.

Leave room for the enlargement!

**2**

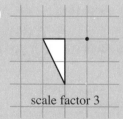

scale factor 3

**3**

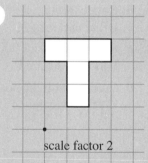

scale factor 2

**4**

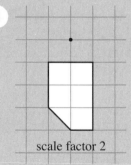

scale factor 2

**5**  **a** Draw the x-axis from −6 to 10.
Draw the y-axis from −3 to 5.
Draw the shape A with vertices at $(-2, 2), (-2, 3), (-1, 3)$,
$(-1, 4), (-4, 4), (-4, 3), (-3, 3), (-3, 2)$.

**b** How many squares does the area of shape A cover?

**c** Enlarge shape A by scale factor 3 about $(-6, 4)$. Label the image B.

**d** How many squares does the area of shape B cover?

**e** Write down how many times bigger the area of the image B is compared to the area of shape A. Compare this to the scale factor.

# NUMBER 3     5

**1**   Work out

| a | 13·0 | b | 14·68 | c | 89·53 | d | 24·7 |
|---|------|---|-------|---|-------|---|------|
|   | − 7·4 |  | + 29·31 |  | − 28·29 |  | 8·2 |
|   |      |   |       |   |       |   | + 37·43 |

**2**   Write down which sets of numbers below add up to 14.

A $\boxed{3·6 + 7·1 + 3·3}$     B $\boxed{8 + 1·9 + 4·1}$

C $\boxed{5·8 + 6·4 + 2·8}$     D $\boxed{3·12 + 6 + 4·88}$

**3**   Which answer below is the larger?

A $\boxed{8·12 − 5·6}$   or   B $\boxed{7·36 − 4·74}$

**4**   How much change from a £10 note do you get if you spend:

  **a** £4·81     **b** £2·64     **c** £8·21     **d** £6·72

**5**   Barney can spend up to £1200 on his credit card. He buys a laptop for £895·99, a desk for £104·95 and a computer game for £34·50. How much more money could he spend using his credit card?

**6**   Work out the following (remember to line up the decimal point):

  **a** 4 + 2·17     **b** 6·84 + 2·19     **c** 51·4 − 17·6

  **d** 28·6 − 15     **e** 49·81 − 16·9     **f** 19 − 4·8

**7**   Work out the difference between 216·4 and 83·26

**8**   Denise has £20. She spends £3·25 on the bus and £4·83 on lunch. How much money does she have left?

**9**   Which answer below is the smaller?

A $\boxed{5 − 2·42}$   or   B $\boxed{19 − 16·52}$

**10**

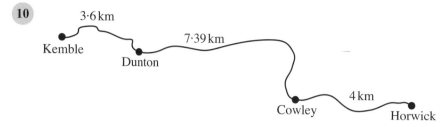

How far is it from Kemble to Horwick?

**11** In a cafe, Parker buys 3 sandwiches, one pot of tea and 2 cups of coffee.
The total bill is £18·85. A sandwich costs £4·25 and a pot of tea costs £1·80.
How much does one cup of coffee cost?

**12** $51·8 - \boxed{?} = 24·53$

Work out the value of ?

**13** Find the perimeter of this pentagon.

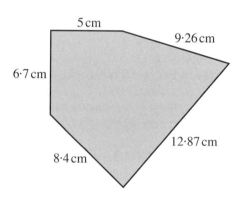

**14** Colin runs a race in 47·28 seconds. Donna runs the race in 51·1 seconds.
By how many seconds did Colin win the race?

---

**TASK M5.2** | **Main Book Page 153**

**1** For each question below write 'True' or 'False'
  **a** $0·6 \times 0·3 = 0·18$  **b** $0·8 \times 0·6 = 0·48$   **c** $0·4 \times 0·08 = 0·032$  **d** $8 \times 0·05 = 0·4$

**2** Work out
  **a** $7 \times 0·3$        **b** $-0·7 \times 0·5$       **c** $-0·9 \times -0·3$
  **d** $0·06 \times 0·9$     **e** $0·08 \times 7$         **f** $0·4^2$

**3** Work out
  **a** $£1·76 \times 3$      **b** $£3·64 \times 4$       **c** $£7·13 \times 8$

**4** Find the total cost of 4 packets of washing powder at £3·28 for each packet.

**5** 5 people each weigh 68·7 kg. What is their total weight?

**6** Which answer below is the correct answer?

    **a** $1.8 \times 0.7 = 1.26$      or      **b** $1.8 \times 0.7 = 12.6$

**7** Work out

    **a** $5.9 \times 0.4$      **b** $-26 \times 0.07$      **c** $34 \times 0.03$

    **d** $-0.17 \times -0.5$      **e** $1.3 \times 0.08$      **f** $2.51 \times -0.9$

**8** A packet of 9 toilet rolls costs £4·18. A family use 5 toilet rolls each week.
How many packets must be bought to cover 10 weeks and what will be the total cost?

**9** Work out

    **a** $6 \times 0.1$      **b** $29 \times -0.01$      **c** $0.4 \times 0.1$      **d** $13 \times 0.1$

    **e** $0.71 \times 0.1$      **f** $-48 \times -0.01$      **g** $-631 \times 0.01$      **h** $0.8 \times 0.1$

**10** £1 = €1·68. Change £15 into Euros by multiplying by 1·68.

**11** Copy and fill in the empty boxes

    **a** $5.6 \times \square = 0.56$      **b** $384 \times \square = 3.84$      **c** $-82 \times \square = 0.82$

    **d** $3.9 \times \square = 0.039$      **e** $\square \times -0.1 = -0.6$      **f** $\square \times 0.01 = 0.34$

---

**TASK M5.3**                               **Main Book Page 154**

**1** Work out

    **a** $4 \overline{)24.8}$      **b** $6 \overline{)12.84}$      **c** $4 \overline{)32.20}$

    **d** $5 \overline{)28.0}$      **e** $2 \overline{)19.0}$      **f** $8 \overline{)13.000}$

**2** Divide the following numbers by 4

    **a** $9.52$      **b** $23$      **c** $55$      **d** $4.5$

**3** Maggy, Jack, Janet and Wasim go to a rock concert. The total cost of the tickets is £62·60.
What is the cost of one ticket?

**4** 6 cans of beer cost £6·48. How much does one can of beer cost?

**5** Work out

    **a** $11.4 \div 6$      **b** $30.7 \div 5$      **c** $-41.92 \div 8$

    **d** $34.48 \div 4$      **e** $4.83 \div 7$      **f** $-0.234 \div 9$

    **g** $-26.6 \div 8$      **h** $0.156 \div 5$      **i** $-14.04 \div 6$

**6** A multipack of tins of baked beans costs £1·56. The multipack contains 4 tins of baked beans.
A single can of baked beans can be bought for 45p each. Which is the better price for one tin of
baked beans and by how much?

**7** A pair of AA batteries costs £1·92. A pack of 8 AA batteries costs £7·44.
Tom needs to buy 16 AA batteries. Is it cheaper to buy pairs of batteries or packs of 8?
Show working out to explain your answer clearly.

---

**TASK M5.4** ──────────────────────────────── **Main Book Page 156**

**1** Which of the numbers below are correctly rounded off to the number of decimal places shown:

   **a** $3·68 \rightarrow 3·6$ (to 1 decimal place)       **b** $5·74 \rightarrow 5·7$ (to 1 decimal place)

   **c** $5·53 \rightarrow 5·5$ (to 1 decimal place)       **d** $8·264 \rightarrow 8·27$ (to 2 decimal places)

   **e** $6·828 \rightarrow 6·83$ (to 2 decimal places)    **f** $17·614 \rightarrow 17·6$ (to 1 decimal place)

**2** Round these numbers to 2 decimal places.

   **a** $4·814$      **b** $0·363$      **c** $28·1894$      **d** $5·645$

**3** 10 800 people live in the city of Wells (to the nearest 100).
Write down the least number of people that might live in Wells.

**4** Which numbers opposite
round to 6·74
(to 2 decimal places)?

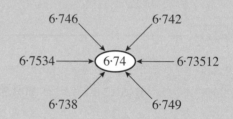

**5** 75 000 people went on a protest march. If this number had been rounded to the nearest 1000, write down the lowest number of people that might have been on the protest march.

**6** Hailey rounds off 12·316 to 2 decimal places. Mason rounds off 19·849 to 1 decimal place. Work out the difference between their two final answers.

**7** Work out these answers on a *calculator* and then round the answers to the accuracy shown.

   **a** $4·16 \times 2·7$ (to 1 decimal place)      **b** $14·6 \div 7$ (to 2 decimal places)

   **c** $284 \div 31$ (to 1 decimal place)       **d** $0·387^2$ (to 2 decimal places)

   **e** $9 \div 0·53$ (to 3 decimal places)       **f** $\sqrt{29}$ (to 2 decimal places)

   **e** $(7·16 - 3·49)^2$ (to 3 decimal places)   **f** $0·72 \times 0·81 \times 0·3$ (to 3 decimal places)

**TASK M5.5** ————————————————————

**1** 5·3 × 7·8 = 41·34. Is this likely to be correct?
5·3 × 7·8 is roughly 5 × 8 = 40 so the answer 41·34 is likely to be correct.
Write down which answers below are likely to be correct by finding sensible **rough** answers.
*Do not use a calculator.*

**a** 4·8 × 88 = 422·4

**b** 7·9 × 12·85 = 1015·15

**c** 58·16 − 17·96 = 40·2

**d** $8·04^2 = 646·416$

**e** 19·9 × 30·14 = 59·9786

**f** $2·06^3 = 874·1816$

**2** *Estimate* the area of this rectangle.

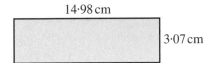
14·98 cm
3·07 cm

**3** A shop sells 47 selection boxes for Christmas. Each selection box costs £3·89.
*Estimate* how much money the shop receives for the selection boxes.

**4** A rectangular room measures 6·2 m by 4·84 m. Carpet costs £19·95 per square metre.
*Estimate* how much it will cost to carpet the room.

**5** *Do not use a calculator.*
Use sensible rough answers to match each question below to the correct answer:

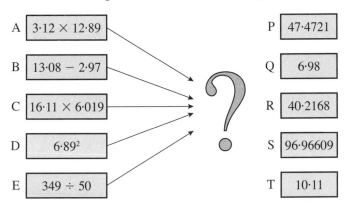

A | 3·12 × 12·89

B | 13·08 − 2·97

C | 16·11 × 6·019

D | $6·89^2$

E | 349 ÷ 50

P | 47·4721

Q | 6·98

R | 40·2168

S | 96·96609

T | 10·11

**6** If 47 × 368 = 17 296, work out the value of:

**a** 4·7 × 3·68

**b** 17 296 ÷ 368

**c** 17·296 ÷ 3·68

**TASK M5.6** ——————————————————— **Main Book Page 161**

*Use a calculator.*

**1** Work out

   **a** $-9 \div (-3)$       **b** $-5 \cdot 6 \times -4 \cdot 7$       **c** $-8 \cdot 1 \times -17$

   **d** $(2 \cdot 8 + 3 \cdot 4) \times 0 \cdot 9$       **e** $4 \cdot 6 \times (6 \cdot 2 - 3 \cdot 7)$       **f** $2 \cdot 63^2$

**2** Work out the following and give your answer *in pounds*.

   **a** £4·15 × 4       **b** £3·80 × 9       **c** £230·52 ÷ 17

   **d** 160 × 3p       **e** £7·60 × 12       **f** 14p × 270

**3** Each of the calculations below is wrong.
Find the correct answer for each calculation.

   **a** $\dfrac{48 + 32}{20} = 49 \cdot 6$       **b** $\dfrac{51 - 31}{10} = 47 \cdot 9$

   **c** $\dfrac{50}{25 \times 10} = 20$       **d** $\dfrac{75}{40 - 20} = -18 \cdot 125$

**4** Work out the following, giving answers to the *nearest whole number*.
Match each calculation to the correct answer.

A $\left( 16 + 4 \cdot 9 - 3 \cdot 17 \right)$        P $\boxed{7}$

B $\left( 3 \cdot 4 \times (5 \cdot 8 - 4 \cdot 25) \right)$        Q $\boxed{4}$

C $\left( 8 \cdot 7 + \dfrac{2 \cdot 4}{1 \cdot 6} \right)$        R $\boxed{18}$

D $\left( \dfrac{35 \cdot 2}{(4 \cdot 9 - 0 \cdot 18)} \right)$        S $\boxed{10}$

E $\left( \dfrac{24 \cdot 63}{(2 \cdot 17 + 3 \cdot 42)} \right)$        T $\boxed{3}$

F $\left( \dfrac{13 \cdot 8 + 9 \cdot 16}{2 \cdot 4 \times 3 \cdot 7} \right)$        U $\boxed{5}$

**TASK M5.7** ——————————————————— **Main Book Page 162**

*Use a calculator* to work out

**1**   **a** $\dfrac{4}{5} - \dfrac{2}{3}$       **b** $\dfrac{4}{9} \div \dfrac{1}{3}$       **c** $1\dfrac{1}{5} \times 3\dfrac{2}{7}$       **d** $4\dfrac{1}{2} \div 1\dfrac{5}{6}$

**2** Work out

a $3 \cdot 4^2$      b $\sqrt{0 \cdot 49}$      c $\sqrt{13 \cdot 69}$      d $(7 + 9)^2$

e $8^3$      f $\sqrt{38 \cdot 44}$      g $4^5$      h $\sqrt[3]{729}$

**3** 27 minutes $= \dfrac{27}{60}$ of an hour $= 27 \div 60 = 0 \cdot 45$ hours.

Write these time intervals *in hours* as decimals.

a 24 minutes      b 33 minutes      c 57 minutes

d 3 hours 15 minutes      e 2 hours 6 minutes      f 5 hours 42 minutes

**4** Work out and give each answer correct to 2 decimal places.

a $\dfrac{17 \cdot 46}{(4 \cdot 17 + 0 \cdot 8)}$      b $8 \cdot 623 + 4 \cdot 9^2$      c $2 \cdot 6^2 \times (9 \cdot 83 - 1 \cdot 64)$

d $\dfrac{13 \cdot 6 + 19 \cdot 5}{2 \cdot 74}$      e $\dfrac{34 \cdot 16}{3 \cdot 6 \times 1 \cdot 7}$      f $\dfrac{17 \cdot 2 + 8 \cdot 16}{8 \cdot 61 - 2 \cdot 48}$

g $\sqrt{\dfrac{23 \cdot 7 + 41 \cdot 18}{4 \cdot 68}}$      h $\dfrac{5 \cdot 8^3 + 3 \cdot 29}{3 \cdot 6^2 - 1 \cdot 92}$      i $\sqrt{\dfrac{2 \cdot 93^2}{5 \cdot 4 \times 2 \cdot 18}}$

**5** Copy and fill in the empty boxes:

a $\dfrac{5}{9} \times \boxed{\phantom{x}} = \dfrac{20}{63}$      b $3\dfrac{1}{2} - \boxed{\phantom{x}} = 1\dfrac{5}{6}$      c $\boxed{\phantom{x}} \div \dfrac{4}{7} = 1\dfrac{1}{6}$

d $\boxed{\phantom{x}} + 2\dfrac{1}{3} = 2\dfrac{17}{24}$      e $4\dfrac{1}{2} \times \boxed{\phantom{x}} = 14\dfrac{2}{5}$      f $\boxed{\phantom{x}} \div 1\dfrac{1}{2} = 1\dfrac{5}{6}$

---

**TASK M5.8** ———————————————————— **Main Book Page 164**

**1** Write the numbers below correct to 3 significant figures.

a $3 \cdot 168$      b $5 \cdot 6163$      c $41 \cdot 689$      d $0 \cdot 1472$

e $16 \cdot 594$      f $61\,749$      g $26\,447$      h $317 \cdot 58$

**2** Which of the numbers below round to 37 200 (to 3 significant figures)?

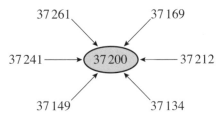

**3** Which numbers below are correctly rounded off to 2 significant figures?

**a** $5·65 = 5·7$      **b** $4189 = 4100$      **c** $0·0176 = 0·018$      **d** $0·0607 = 0·061$

**4** $0·075$ has been rounded off to 2 significant figures.
Write down the least possible value of this number before it was rounded off.

**5** *Use a calculator* to work out the following, giving each answer to the number of significant figures shown.

**a** $64 ÷ 3·7$    (3 s.f.)        **b** $20·8 × 11·6$    (2 s.f.)

**c** $(8·14 + 6·5) × 19$    (2 s.f.)        **d** $14·6^2$    (3 s.f.)

**e** $48 − 12·61$    (3 s.f.)        **f** $172 × 486$    (2 s.f.)

**g** $13·63 ÷ 0·18$    (1 s.f.)        **h** $\dfrac{4·8}{(6·4 + 2·34)}$    (2 s.f.)

---

**TASK M5.9**              **Main Book Page 166**

**1** *Estimate*, correct to 1 significant figure:

**a** $6·9 × 10·01$        **b** $28·03 ÷ 6·89$        **c** $19·93^2$

**d** $\dfrac{4·9 + 15·12}{1·961}$        **e** $\dfrac{9·04^2 + 18·87}{20·07}$        **f** $\dfrac{1}{8}$ of £23 998

**g** $\dfrac{3}{4}$ of £79 999        **h** 26% of £12 134        **i** $\dfrac{29·892 + 19·9}{19·94 − 10·103}$

**2** Do *not* use a calculator.
$384 × 27 = 10 368$
Work out

**a** $10 368 ÷ 27$        **b** $10 368 ÷ 384$        **c** $38·4 × 27$

**3** Do *not* use a calculator.
$486 × 147 = 71 442$
Work out

**a** $71 442 ÷ 147$        **b** $48·6 × 14·7$        **c** $4·86 × 14·7$

**4** Do *not* use a calculator.
$37 107 ÷ 63 = 589$
Work out

**a** $589 × 63$        **b** $37 107 ÷ 589$        **c** $3710·7 ÷ 6·3$

**5** Makayla works out that $3·60 × 28·3 = 1018·8$.
Explain clearly how Makayla can check without a calculator whether she is correct or not.

**6** Matt says that $\dfrac{4·2}{0·5}$ is $8·4$. Explain clearly how John can check without a calculator whether he is correct or not.

**TASK M5.10** ———————————————————— Main Book Page 168

**1** In a survey 73 out of every 100 people said they loved ice cream. Write down the percentage of people who love ice cream.

**2** 45% of the students in a class said they had been to the cinema in the last month.
What percentage of the students had *not* been to the cinema in the last month?

**3** 68% of men drink alcohol at least once during the week. What percentage of the men do *not* drink alcohol at least once during the week?

**4** **a** What percentage of the large square is shaded?
**b** What percentage of the large square is *not* shaded?

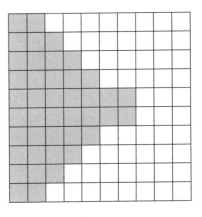

**5** 53 out of every 100 children walk to school each day.
What percentage of children do *not* walk to school?

**6** Change these percentages into fractions. Cancel the answers when possible
$\left( \text{example: } 46\% = \dfrac{46}{100} = \dfrac{23}{50} \right).$

| | | | | | |
|---|---|---|---|---|---|
| **a** 17% | **b** 20% | **c** 29% | **d** 12% | **e** 25% | **f** 60% |
| **g** 24% | **h** 35% | **i** 88% | **j** 32% | **k** 9% | **l** 95% |

**7** 2% of semi-skimmed milk is fat. What fraction of semi-skimmed milk is fat?

**8** Change these fractions into percentages (remember: multiply by 100 unless you can see a quicker way).

**a** $\dfrac{7}{10}$   **b** $\dfrac{2}{5}$   **c** $\dfrac{3}{25}$   **d** $\dfrac{38}{50}$   **e** $\dfrac{13}{20}$   **f** $\dfrac{8}{25}$

**9** Katherine scored $\dfrac{18}{20}$ in a maths test.

Luka scored 92% and Lillian had a score of $\dfrac{22}{25}$. Who scored the highest percentage mark?

Show working out to explain your answer.

**10** Elmer scored 17 out of 20 for English coursework. What percentage was this?

**1**   19 out of 20 pupils in a class go on a school trip. What percentage of the class go on a school trip?

**2**   What percentage of these boxes contain:

     **a**   crosses

     **b**   circles

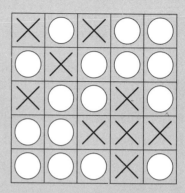

**3**   **a**   Write 19 as a percentage of 50.

     **b**   Write 11 as a percentage of 20.

     **c**   Write 300 as a percentage of 500.

**4**   In a survey 120 people were asked if they had internet access at home. 96 people said 'yes'. What percentage of the people said they had internet access at home?

**5**   150 students were asked where their home town was.
The findings are shown in this table.
What percentage of the students came from:

     **a**   Wales         **b**   The North

     **c**   Ireland       **d**   The Midlands

| Home area | Number of students |
|---|---|
| Wales | 45 |
| The South | 24 |
| The Midlands | 27 |
| The North | 36 |
| Scotland | 6 |
| Ireland | 12 |
| Total | 150 |

*For the remaining questions use a calculator and give your answers to the nearest whole number.*

**6**   28 out of 43 young people at a Youth club one evening are male.
What percentage of the young people are male?

**7**   Sunita is given £60 for her birthday. She spends £47 on computer games.
What percentage of her birthday money has she got left?

**8**   What percentage of these letters is the letter 'K'?

                                        O K
                              O K    O K
                          O K         O K
                                  O K    K
                              O K    O K

**9** Tamsin scored 39 out of 47 in a Science test. Peter scored 47 out of 58 in his Science test. Who scored the higher percentage and by how much?

**10** The table shows how some of a 30 g serving of sultana bran cereal is made up. What percentage of the 30 g serving is:

| | |
|---|---|
| fat | 2·6 g |
| sugars | 16 g |
| salt | 0·5 g |
| saturated fat | 1·4 g |

   **a** fat      **b** sugars
   **c** salt      **d** saturated fat

**11** The population of Glastonbury in Somerset is about 10 000. The population of the UK is about 60 000 000. What percentage of the UK's population live in Glastonbury (give your answer to 2 decimal places)?

**12** 34 million people voted in a recent General Election. 13 260 000 people voted Conservative and 11 900 000 people voted Labour.
Find the percentage difference between the number of people who voted Conservative compared to Labour.

---

**TASK M5.12** ─────────────────────────── **Main Book Page 173**

*Do not use a calculator.*

**1** Terry earns £260 a week. Each week he gives 5% of his money to charity. How much money does he give each week?

**2** Find the odd one out
   **a** 30% of £30      **b** 5% of £160      **c** 25% of £32

**3** **a** Increase £40 by 10%.      **b** Decrease £70 by 20%.
   **c** Decrease £50 by 40%.      **d** Increase £28 by 75%.

**4** Kate earns £340 each week. She is given a pay rise of 5%.
How much does she now earn each year?

**5** A laptop costs £1240. One year later it costs 20% less. How much does the laptop cost now?

**6** What is the sale price of each item below?

   **a**
   Sofa £800
   SALE
   30% off

   **b**
   Dishwasher £480
   SALE
   25% off

   **c**
   DVD player £60
   SALE
   15% off

**7** A car costs £24 000. A year later its price has decreased by 3%.
How much does the car cost now?

**8** Increase £800 by 17·5%.

> Find 10% then 5% then 2·5% and add them all together

**9** VAT is value added tax. This tax is added to the cost of items. VAT is usually 20%.
  **a** Find 20% of £360
  **b** Find the cost of a washing machine which costs £360 + VAT.

**10** Henry gets two quotes for an extension to his house (VAT = 20%).
  [1] £16 000 + VAT        [2] £18 500 including VAT
  Which is the cheaper quote? Explain your answer clearly.

**11** Laura earns 30% of what she sells. Last year she sold £120 000 of goods.
  This year she sells 5% more goods than last year.
  How much more money does she earn this year compared to last year?

---

**TASK M5.13** | **Main Book Page 175**

*Use a calculator when needed. Give answers to the nearest penny when needed.*

**1** The garages of 1600 houses were examined. 23% of the garages had yellow doors.
  How many garages had yellow doors?

**2** Work out, correct to the nearest penny:
  **a** 13% of £24·20    **b** 37% of £41·60    **c** 19% of £36·14    **d** 4·8% of £83

**3** Carl's caravan is worth £15 500. One year later it is worth 6% less.
  How much is the caravan now worth?

**4** A cinema increases its prices by 8%. If a ticket was £6·50, what would it cost after the increase?

**5** **a** Decrease £70 by 3%.            **b** Increase £68 by 2%.
  **c** Decrease £264 by 46%.           **d** Increase £89 by 12%.

**6** A tin of baked beans costs 42p. Its price increases by 9% over the next 12 months.
  How much will the tin cost now? (remember to give your answer to the nearest penny)

**7** A new car exhaust costs £146 + VAT. If VAT is 20%, work out the total cost of the car exhaust.

**8** If VAT is 20%, find the price including VAT of each of the following:

  **a** microwave £126        **b** carpet £870

  **c** digital camera £220    **d** kettle £34

**9** An eternity ring costs £680 + VAT (20%).

  **a** What is the total price of the ring?

  **b** In the Summer sales, the price of the ring is reduced by 20%.
  How much does the ring cost in the sales?

**10** 40 people plan to pay £468 to hire a coach for a trip. They will each pay the same amount of money. Eventually 35% of the people decide not to go on the trip.
How much extra must each person pay if the remaining people still want to hire the coach?

---

| **TASK E5.1** | **Main Book Page 178** |

**1** Increase £130 by 40%. Which calculation below will give the answer?

| A | 1·04 × 130 |    | B | 130 × 40 |    | C | 1·4 × 130 |    | D | 0·6 × 130 |

**2** Decrease £250 by 20%. Which calculation below will give the answer?

| A | 0·8 × 250 |    | B | 1·2 × 250 |    | C | 0·2 × 250 |    | D | 0·08 × 250 |

**3** £420 is to be increased by 5%. Look at the list below and choose the multiplier which should be used for this calculation.

( 1·5 )  ( 0·95 )  ( 0·05 )  ( 1·05 )  ( 0·42 )  ( 0·5 )

**4** Use a multiplier to do the following:

  **a** Increase £90 by 30%     **b** Decrease £160 by 5%

  **c** Reduce £140 by 60%      **d** Increase £240 by 20%

**5** VAT is 20%. Use a multiplier to work out the total cost of a new dining table which costs £650 + VAT.

**6** 2 years ago Colton Electrics made a profit of £130 000. Last year the profit increased by 30%. This year the profit went down by 40% of last year's profit. Work out this year's profit.

**7** A DVD player is £68 + VAT (20%).
The shop increases all its prices by 15%.
Find the new total cost of the DVD player.

> Remember: The price of a TV is increased by 30% and now it costs £572.
> What was the original price?
> Increase = 30% so multiplier = 100% + 30% = 130% = 1·3
> *Reverse* the percentage so original price  = £572 ÷ 1·3
>  = £440

**1** The price of a computer game is increased by 40% and now costs £81·20. Find
a the multiplier  b the original price

**2** The cost of a computer decreases by 10% and now costs £558. Find
a the multiplier  b the original cost

**3** VAT at 20% has been added onto the cost of each item shown below.

| fridge | £336 |
|---|---|
| washing machine | £468 |
| freezer | £288 |

Work out the cost of each item before VAT was added.

**4** The value of a car decreases by 20% after one year and is now worth £6800.
What was the value of the car one year earlier?

**5** A skirt shrinks in the wash. Its length decreases by 10% and is now 30.6 cm long.
What was the length of the skirt before it went in the wash?

**6** Which item in the table below was the most expensive before the price changes?
You must show all your working out.

| Item | % change | New price |
|---|---|---|
| microwave | 10% decrease | £40·50 |
| toaster | 20% increase | £38·40 |
| radio | 50% decrease | £27·50 |
| iron | 30% increase | £36·40 |

**7** This year the population of Henton High School increases by 10% on last year to 1320.
The population of Colton College decreases by 20% on last year to 1280.
How many more students were in Colton College last year compared to Henton High
School?

**TASK M5.14** ———————————————————————— **Main Book Page 181**

1 Change these percentages into decimals:

    **a** 47%      **b** 21%      **c** 80%      **d** 36%      **e** 4%      **f** 7%

2 Change these decimals into percentages:

    **a** 0·59      **b** 0·23      **c** 0·03      **d** 0·3      **e** 0·2      **f** 0·18

3 Match up equivalent fractions, decimals and percentages. (You should find 5 groups of 3 numbers and there is one number on its own)

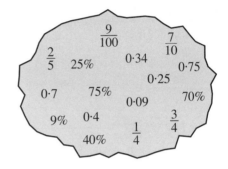

4 Which of the following are true?

    **a** 4% = 0·4      **b** 60% = 0·6      **c** 0·2 = 20%      **d** 0·03 = 3%

    **e** 80% = 0·8      **f** 0·07 = 70%      **g** 0·9 = 90%      **h** 2% = 0·02

5 '0·4 is greater than 39%'. Is this correct? Explain your answer fully.

**TASK M5.15** ———————————————————————— **Main Book Page 183**

1 Find the simple interest on £1500 at 4% per annum for 2 years.

$$\text{simple interest} = \frac{PRT}{100}$$

where P = money invested or borrowed (the principal)

R = rate of the interest per year

T = number of years

2 Find the simple interest on £2400 at 5% per annum for 6 years.

3 Megan borrows £10 000 to buy a car. She is charged 7% per annum simple interest. She pays back all the money in 7 years. How much does she pay back in total?

4 Ben borrows £800 to buy a computer. He repays all the money over 5 years with a simple interest rate of 8% per annum. He pays back an equal amount each month. How much will each monthly payment be?

5 Find the simple interest on £3000 at 5% per annum for 6 months.

**6** Two amounts of money are invested at the simple interest rate shown below. Which account will have more money in it after the amount of time shown and by how much?

| Account A |
|---|
| £8000 at 9% for 5 years |

| Account B |
|---|
| £9500 at 6% for 3 years |

**7** Charlotte borrows £6000 for her educational studies. She is charged 5·99% per annum simple interest and must pay the money back in 7 years. She pays back an equal amount each month. How much will each monthly payment be?

**8** Find the simple interest on £4500 at 6% per annum for 4 years 3 months.

**TASK M5.16/M5.17** ──────────────────────── **Main Book Page 185**

**1.** Copy and complete each sentence below:

**a** 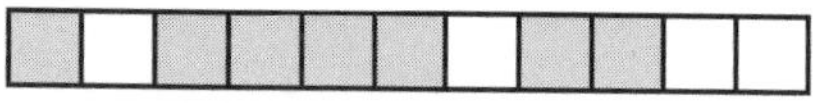  The ratio black to white is □ : □

**b** 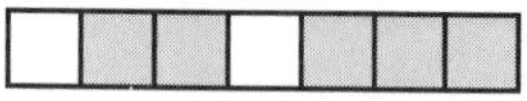  The ratio black to white is □ : □

**2** For each diagram below, write down the ratio of black to white in its simplest form.

**a** 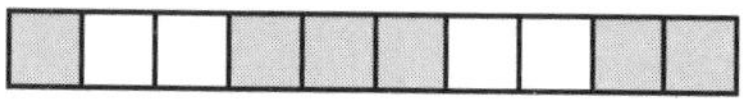  **b**

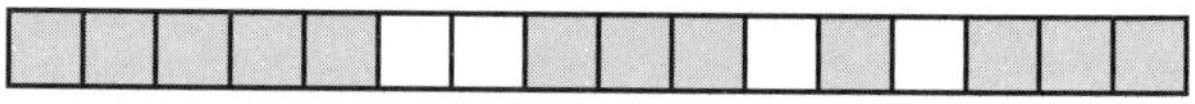

**3** Copy the diagrams and colour them in to match the given ratio.

**a** 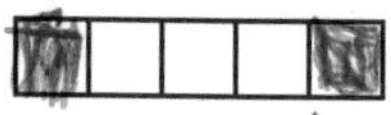  The ratio black to white is 2 : 3.

**b** 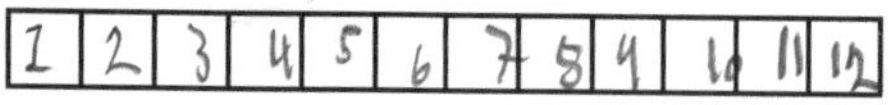  The ratio black to white is 2 : 1.

**4** In a swimming pool there are 30 people. 20 of the people are male. Find the ratio of males to females. Give the ratio in its simplest form.

**5** In a box there are 14 pens and 6 pencils. Find the ratio of pens to pencils in its simplest form.

**6** The ratio of boys to girls in a class is 3 : 4. If there are 12 boys, how many girls are there?

**7** The ratio of blond haired people to dark haired people is 5 to 2. If there are 6 dark haired people, how many blond haired people are there?

**8** Change the following ratios to their simplest form.

    **a** 8 : 10         **b** 30 : 40         **c** 12 : 30         **d** 63 : 27

    **e** 32 : 28         **f** 12 : 9 : 21      **g** 50 cm : 4 m     **h** 25p : £3

9   Is the ratio 24 : 36 equivalent to 18 : 27? Explain your answer fully.

> **Remember:**
>
> To remove the decimal 1·8 from the
> ratio 1·8 : 5, multiply both numbers
> by 10. 1·8 : 5 = 18 : 50
> This can be simplified to 9 : 25

10  Write each ratio below in their simplest
    whole number form

   a  1·2 : 1·5          b  3·2 : 4

   c  2·7 : 4·5          d  8·4 : 2·4

   e  1·75 : 0·5         f  5 : 2·25

11  Yuri says that the ratio 2·4 : 1·8 : 4·2 is equivalent to 6 : 4·5 : 10·5. Michelle does not agree.
    Who is correct? Give reasons for your answer.

---

**TASK M5.18** ———————————————————————— **Main Book Page 188**

1   7 books costs £42. How much will 9 books cost?

2   8 hats cost £56. How much will 7 hats cost?

3   3 dishwashers cost £1245. What do 5 dishwashers cost?

4   4 calculators cost £23·96. How much will 7 calculators cost?

5   13 people pay £89·70 to visit a castle. How much would 28 people have to pay?

6   Mindy used 550 g of lamb to make a curry for 8 people. How much lamb would she have to
    use to make curry for 12 people?

7   Cheese kebabs for 4 people need the ingredients below:

| 220 g | cheese |
|---|---|
| 4 | tomatoes |
| 8 | pineapple chunks |
| $\frac{1}{2}$ | cucumber |

   How much of each ingredient is needed for 10 people?

8   400 g of cheese costs £4·60.
    500 g of cheese costs £5·80.
    Which weight of cheese is the better buy? Explain your answer fully.

9   160 g of cat food costs £2·80.
    400 g of cat food costs £6·80.
    Which is the better value? Explain your answer fully.

10  Evan changes £120 for €148·80 at the nearest bank. How many euros would he get for £150
    at the same bank?

**11** The recipe for making 20 biscuits is given below:

| 120 g | butter |
|-------|--------|
| 50 g | caster sugar |
| 175 g | flour |

How much of each ingredient is needed for 24 biscuits?

**12** A 200 g box of washing powder costs £2·20.

A $\frac{3}{4}$ kg box of washing powder costs £7·95.

Which is the better value? Explain your answer fully.

---

**TASK M5.19** ──────────────────────────── **Main Book Page 191**

**1** **a** Divide £150 in the ratio 1 : 4      **b** Divide £60 in the ratio 3 : 2

   **c** Divide 49g in the ratio 2 : 5      **d** Divide 96 kg in the ratio 5 : 3

   **e** Divide £900 in the ratio 6 : 1 : 3      **f** Divide 75 litres in the ratio 4 : 5 : 6

**2** Todd and Claire receive a total of 30 christmas presents in the ratio 3 : 7.
How many presents do each of them receive?

**3** A man leaves £12 000 to Carl and Rachel in the ratio 5 : 1. How much will each person get?

**4** The angles $p$, $q$ and $r$ are in the ratio 7 : 2 : 3.
Find the sizes of the angles $p$, $q$ and $r$.

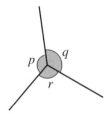

**5** There are 45 000 fans at a football match involving Aston Villa and Birmingham City.
The ratio of Aston Villa to Birmingham City fans is 5 : 4. How many Aston Villa fans are at the
football match?

**6** Orange squash is diluted with water in the ratio 1 : 7. If 84 ml of water is used, how much
orange squash is needed?

**1** A paint mixed by using yellow and blue in the ratio 7 : 2

  **a** How much yellow is used if 8 litres of blue are used?

  **b** How much blue is used if 35 litres of yellow are used?

  **c** How much yellow and how much blue must be used to make 72 litres of the paint?

**2** If $\frac{6}{11}$ of the children in a class are boys, what is the ratio of boys to girls?

**3** Some money is left to Will and Dido in the ratio 9 : 11. If Will gets £240 less than Dido, how much will Dido get?

**4** Des, Simone and Julie earn money in the ratio 3 : 2 : 5. If Des earns £27 000 each year, how much do Simone and Julie each earn?

**5** Ginny and Ben have collected 'Warhammer' pieces in the ratio 7 : 4. If Ginny has 63 pieces, how many pieces do they have in *total*?

**6** Amelia and her brother share out some sweets in the ratio 7 : 4. Amelia has 18 sweets more than her brother.
Amelia's sweets are yellow, pink and blue in the ratio 1 : 3 : 2.
If Amelia eats 4 pink sweets, how many pink sweets does she have left?

**7** 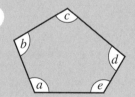 The angles in a pentagon add up to 540°.
The angles $a : b : c : d : e$ are in the ratio 7 : 5 : 3 : 8 : 4
How much larger is angle $d$ compared to angle $c$?

**8** Ellie, Dan and Lewis own DVD's in the ratio 14 : 5 : 9. If Lewis owns 81 DVD's, how many DVD's do they own in total?

**9** Caroline, Logan and Andrea share some money in the ratio 4 : 9 : 3. Logan gets £350 more than Caroline. Andrea spends two-thirds of her money on some clothes. How much does Andrea have left?

**10** Peter uses a store card. He is rewarded with a £5 voucher every time he spends £100 six times.

  **a** How many £5 vouchers does Peter get if he spends £100 twenty times?

  **b** What is the least number of times he must spend £100 if he receives £30 worth of vouchers?

# ALGEBRA 2      7

In questions **1** to **8**, **a** copy the sequence and write the next 2 numbers, **b** what is the rule for the sequence? **c** is this an arithmetic sequence?

**1**   5, 8, 11, 14, …

**2**   8, 20, 32, 44, …

**3**   44, 39, 34, 29, …

**4**   3, 4, 6, 9, …

**5**   61, 52, 43, 34, …

**6**   10, 15, 25, 40, …

**7**   11, 5, −1, −7, …

**8**   14, 8, 2, −4, …

**9**   You are given the first term of an arithmetic sequence and the rule. Write down the first 5 terms of each sequence.

     **a**   First term = 7      Rule:   add 8

     **b**   First term = 61      Rule:   subtract 7

     **c**   First term = 19      Rule:   subtract 5

In questions **10** to **13** write down the missing numbers.

**10**   22, 19, ☐, 13, ☐

**11**   5, 12, ☐, 26, ☐

**12**   −9, −5, ☐, ☐, 7

**13**   ☐, 20, 14, 8, ☐

**14**   How many dots are needed for

     **a**   shape 4

     **b**   shape 5

Shape 1      Shape 2      Shape 3

**15**   How many squares are needed for

     **a**   shape 5

     **b**   shape 6

Shape 1      Shape 2      Shape 3      Shape 4

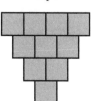

**16** The first four terms of a sequence are 2, 8, 14, 20.
The 50th term in the sequence is 296.
Write down the 49th term.

**17** Shape 1     Shape 2 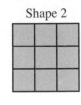    Shape 3 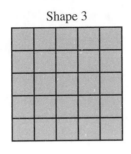    Shape 4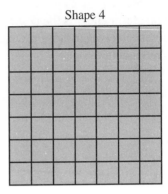

How many small
squares are needed for

**a** shape 5

**b** shape 6

In questions **18** to **21** find the next 2 numbers in each sequence (it may help you to work out the 2nd differences).

**18** 2, 5, 10, 17, …

**19** 0, 3, 8, 15, …

**20** 2, 6, 12, 20, …

**21** 2, 8, 16, 26, …

**22** The first five terms of a sequence are 1, 2, 4, 8, 16, …
The 9th term in the sequence is 512.
Write down the 10th term of the sequence.

**23** Find the next 2 numbers in the sequence below.
Try to explain the pattern.
0, 1, 3, 7, 15, …

---

**TASK M7.2**        **Main Book Page 213**

**1** Write down the *term-to-term* rule for each sequence below:
  **a** 3, 12, 48, 192, …     **b** 53, 45, 37, 29, …
  **c** 9, 6·5, 4, 1·5, …     **d** 2, 5, 14, 41, 122, …

**2** The $n$th term of a sequence is given by the formula $n$th term $= 2n + 1$.
Use values of $n$ from 1 to 5 to write down the first 5 terms of the sequence.

**3** Use each $n$th term formula below to find the first 5 terms of each sequence.
  **a** $n$th term $= 3n + 5$     **b** $n$th term $= 4n - 1$     **c** $n$th term $= 2n + 7$

**Remember:**

$n$th term $= a + (n - 1)d$ for all arithmetic sequences where $a$ is the first term and $d$ is the common difference between successive terms in the sequence.

**4** Here is a sequence: 5, 8, 11, 14, …
The first term is 5 and the common difference is $+3$.
$n$th term $= a + (n - 1)d = 5 + (n - 1) \times 3$.
Multiply out the bracket and write the $n$th term in its simplest form.

**5** Here is a sequence: 2, 7, 12, 17, …
Write down **a** the first term, **b** the common difference, **c** the $n$th term in its simplest form.

**6** Match up each sequence to the correct $n$th term formula.

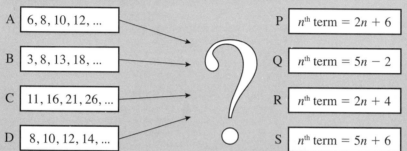

A | 6, 8, 10, 12, …

B | 3, 8, 13, 18, …

C | 11, 16, 21, 26, …

D | 8, 10, 12, 14, …

P | $n^{th}$ term $= 2n + 6$

Q | $n^{th}$ term $= 5n - 2$

R | $n^{th}$ term $= 2n + 4$

S | $n^{th}$ term $= 5n + 6$

**7** For each sequence below, write down the first term and common difference then use them to find the $n$th term .

**a** 7, 10, 13, 16, …        **b** 9, 16, 23, 30, …        **c** 1, 10, 19, 26, …

**d** 6, 14, 22, 30, …        **e** 30, 26, 22, 18, …        **f** 18, 13, 8, 3, …

**g** 8, 12, 16, 20, …        **h** 22, 19, 16, 13, …

**TASK M7.3** ——————————————————————— **Main Book Page 215**

**1** Here is a sequence of shapes made from squares.
Let $n$ = shape number and $w$ = number of white squares.

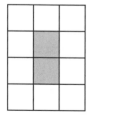
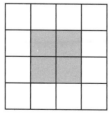
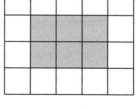

$n = 1$
$w = 10$

$n = 2$
$w = 12$

$n = 3$
$w = 14$

**a** Draw the next shape in the sequence.

**b** How many white squares are in shape number 4?

**c** Complete the table of values.
The first term is 10 and the
common difference is 2.

| $n$ | 1 | 2 | 3 | 4 |
|---|---|---|---|---|
| $w$ | 10 | 12 | 14 | |

Use these to find a formula for the number of white squares ($w$) for the shape number $n$.
Use values of $n$ to check if your formula is correct.

**d** Use your formula to find out how many white squares are in
shape number 50.

**2**

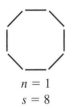

$n = 1$
$s = 8$

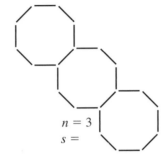

$n = 2$
$s = 15$

$n = 3$
$s =$

**a** Draw the next shape in the sequence.

**b** Let $n$ = shape number and $s$ = number of sticks.
Complete a table of values for $n$ and $s$.

**c** Use the first term and the common difference to find a formula for the number of sticks ($s$)
for the shape number $n$.
Use values of $n$ to check if each formula is correct.

**d** Use the formula to find out how many sticks are in shape number 40.

**3** Repeat question **2** for the sequence below:

$n = 1$

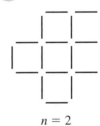

$n = 2$

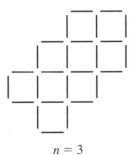

$n = 3$

---

**TASK E7.1** ——————————————————— **Main Book Page 217**

Copy and complete each statement below:

**1** If $a = b + 4$ then $a$ ☐ $4 = b$

**2** If $y = x + 6$ then $y$ ☐ $6 = x$

**3** If $x = 4y$ then $\dfrac{x}{\boxed{\phantom{x}}} = y$

**4** If $a = \dfrac{b}{8}$ then ☐ $a = b$

**5** $a = b - 10$ Make $b$ the subject of the formula.

**6** $n = 5m$ Make $m$ the subject of the formula.

**7** Make $n$ the subject of each formula given below:

**a** $m = n + 9$ **b** $m = 4n$ **c** $m = \dfrac{n}{3}$ **d** $m = n - 10$

**8** Write down the pairs of equations which belong to each other.

$y = 8x$ $y = \dfrac{x}{8}$

$8y = x$ $\dfrac{y}{8} = x$

**9** Write down which working out below is correct.

**a** $m = 4n + 8$
$m + 8 = 4n$
$\dfrac{m + 8}{4} = n$

**b** $y = 2x - 6$
$y + 6 = 2x$
$\dfrac{y + 6}{2} = x$

**10** Make $n$ the subject of each formula given below:

**a** $m = 3n + 5$ **b** $m = 7n - 1$ **c** $m = \dfrac{n}{4} - 6$

**d** $m = 8n - 7$ **e** $m = \dfrac{n}{3} + 9$ **f** $m = \dfrac{n}{5} - 3$

---

**TASK M7.4** | **Main Book Page 218**

**1** **a** Copy this grid.

**b** Draw the line $y = 3$.

**c** Draw the line $y = -2$.

**d** Draw the line $x = 1$.

**e** Write down the co-ordinates where the line $x = 1$ meets the line $y = -2$.

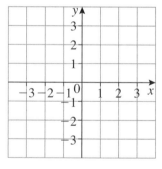

**2** **a** Write down the equation of the line which passes through P and R.

**b** Write down the equation of the line which passes through S and U.

**c** Write down the equation of the line which passes through P and Q.

**d** Write down the equation of the line which passes through W, Q and V.

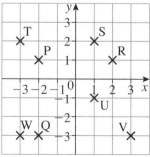

**TASK M7.5** ──────────────────────── | **Main Book Page 220** |

For questions **1** and **2**, you will need to draw axes like these:

**1** Copy and complete the table below then draw the straight line $y = 2x + 1$.

| x | 0 | 1 | 2 | 3 |
|---|---|---|---|---|
| y |   |   | 5 |   |

**2** Copy and complete the table below then draw the straight line $y = 4 - x$.

| x | 0 | 1 | 2 | 3 |
|---|---|---|---|---|
| y |   |   |   |   |

**3** Using x-values from 0 to 4, complete a table then draw the straight line $y = 4x$ (make sure you draw the axes big enough).

For questions **4** and **5**, you will need to draw axes like these:

**4** Copy and complete the table below then draw the straight line $y = 2x - 4$.

| x | −1 | 0 | 1 | 2 | 3 |
|---|---|---|---|---|---|
| y |   |   |   |   |   |

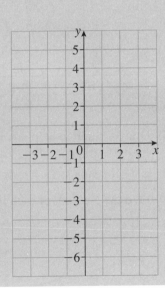

**5** Copy and complete the table below then draw the straight line $y = 3x + 1$.

| x | −2 | −1 | 0 | 1 |
|---|---|---|---|---|
| y |   |   |   |   |

86

Find the gradient of each line.

**1**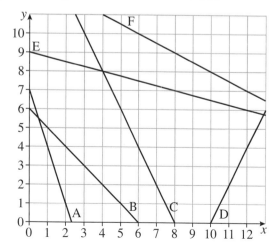

**2**

**Remember:**
Gradient =

$$\frac{\text{vertical distance}}{\text{horizontal distance}}$$

**3**

**4** Draw a graph to help you if you need to.
Find the gradient of the line joining the points:

**a** (1, 1) and (3, 5)    **b** (2, 4) and (3, 7)    **c** (3, 1) and (5, 4)    **d** (1, 0) and (4, 5)

**5** Find the gradient of each line below:

**Remember:** a
line sloping
*downwards* to
the right has a
negative gradient.

**6** Find the gradient of the line joining each pair of points below
(draw a graph to help if you need to):

    **a** (3, 6) and (5, 2)    **b** (1, 4) and (3, 2)    **c** (0, 5) and (2, 4)    **d** (1, 5) and (5, 2)

**7** Find the gradient of each line below (look at the numbers on the axes very carefully):

    **a** 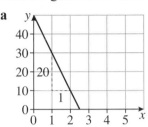    **b**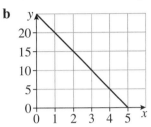

**8** Draw axes on squared paper. Draw a line with gradient $-3$.

---

| TASK M7.7 | Main Book Page 225 |
| --- | --- |

**1** The equation of each line is shown below:

    (**A**) $y = -2x + 6$    (**B**) $y = -2x + 2$

    (**C**) $y = -2x$    (**D**) $y = -2x - 3$

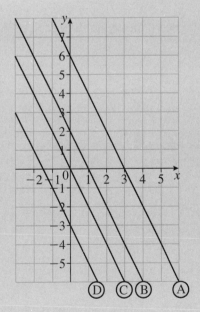

    **a** Use the graph to find the gradient of
lines (A), (B), (C) and (D).

    **b** What do you notice about the gradient
of each line and its equation?

    **c** Look at where each line cuts the $y$-axis.
For each line, what do you notice about
this value and its equation?

**2**  **a** Draw the following lines using the same set of axes:

       $y = 3x + 4$    $y = 3x + 1$    $y = 3x$    $y = 3x - 2$    $y = 3x - 3$

    **b** Find the gradient of each line. What do you notice about the
gradient of each line and its equation?

    **c** Look at where each line cuts the $y$-axis. For each line, what do you
notice about this value and its equation?

88

**1** Which lines below are parallel?

$y = 5x + 1$     $y = 3x + 1$     $y = 1 - 5x$     $y = 5x + 4$     $y = 3 + 5x$

**2** Which lines below cut the $y$-axis at the same point?

$y = 3x + 2$     $y = 2 + 4x$     $y = 3x - 2$     $y = 2x + 3$     $y = 2x$

**3** Write down **i** the gradient and **ii** the $y$-intercept of each line below:

**a** $y = 8x + 4$       **b** $y = 2x - 6$       **c** $y = x$       **d** $y = x - 5$

**e** $y = 4 - 2x$       **f** $y = \frac{1}{4}x + 3$       **g** $y = -3x + 2$       **h** $y = 7x - 6$

**i** $y = \frac{1}{4}x + 5$       **j** $y = 6 - x$       **k** $y = 5 - 3x$       **l** $y = 9 + \frac{1}{6}x$

**4** Write down the equation of each of the 3 lines shown.

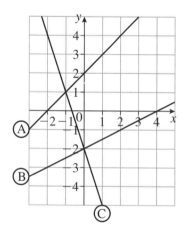

**5** Draw a set of axes then draw a line with gradient 3 and $y$-intercept at $(0, -1)$.

**6** Draw a set of axes then draw a line with gradient $-1$ and $y$-intercept at $(0, -2)$.

**Main Book Page 227**

**1** Find the value of these when $x = -3$:

    **a** $x^2$         **b** $x^2 + 2$         **c** $x^2 - 4$         **d** $x^2 + 2x$         **e** $x^2 - x$

For questions **2** and **3**, you will need to draw axes like these:

**2** Complete the table below then draw the curve $y = x^2 + 2$.

| $x$ | $-3$ | $-2$ | $-1$ | 0 | 1 | 2 | 3 |
|-----|------|------|------|---|---|---|---|
| $y$ |      |      |      |   |   |   |   |

**3** Complete the table below then draw the curve $y = x^2 - 1$.

| $x$ | $-3$ | $-2$ | $-1$ | 0 | 1 | 2 | 3 |
|-----|------|------|------|---|---|---|---|
| $y$ |      |      |      |   |   |   |   |

**4** **a** Complete the table below for $y = 4x^2$
    ($4x^2$ means $x^2$ then 'multiply by 4').

| $x$ | $-2$ | $-1$ | 0 | 1 | 2 |
|-----|------|------|---|---|---|
| $y$ |      |      |   |   |   |

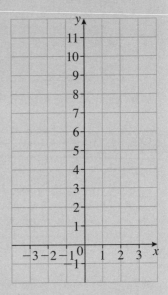

    **b** Draw an $x$-axis from $-3$ to 3 (use 2 cm for 1 unit) and a $y$-axis from 0 to 18 (use 1 cm for 2 units). Draw the curve $y = 4x^2$.

 **Main Book Page 229**

For questions **1** and **2**, you will need to draw axes like those shown opposite:

**1** **a** Complete the table below then draw the curve $y = x^2 + 3x$.

| $x$ | $-3$ | $-2$ | $-1$ | 0 | 1 | 2 | 3 |
|------|------|------|------|---|---|----|---|
| $x^2$ |      |      | 1 |   |   | 4 |   |
| $+3x$ |      |      | $-3$ |   |   | 6 |   |
| $y$ |      |      | $-2$ |   |   | 10 |   |

    **b** Read off the value of $y$ from your graph when $x = 1.5$.

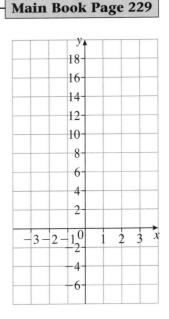

**2** **a** Complete the table below then draw
the curve $y = x^2 + 2x - 5$.

| $x$ | $-3$ | $-2$ | $-1$ | $0$ | $1$ | $2$ | $3$ |
|---|---|---|---|---|---|---|---|
| $x^2$ | 9 | | | | | | |
| $+2x$ | $-6$ | | | | | | |
| $-5$ | $-5$ | | | | | | |
| $y$ | $-2$ | | | | | | |

**b** Read off the value of $x$ from your graph when $y = 0$.

---

**TASK M7.10** | **Main Book Page 229**

**1** A crowd of 8000 people attended
a football match which started
at 3 p.m. The graph on the right
shows the number of people
who had entered the ground at
different times.

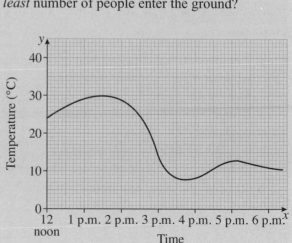

How many people had entered
the ground by the following
times?

**a** 1 p.m.

**b** 1:15 p.m.

**c** 2:15 p.m.

**d** 12:45 p.m.

**e** During which half-hour interval did the *least* number of people enter the ground?

**2** The graph opposite shows the
temperature during a day:

**a** What was the temperature at 1 p.m.?

**b** What was the temperature at
4.30 p.m.?

**c** At what time was the temperature
20 °C?

**d** When was the temperature 15 °C?

**e** When did the temperature start
falling?

**f** How much did it fall by?

**1**

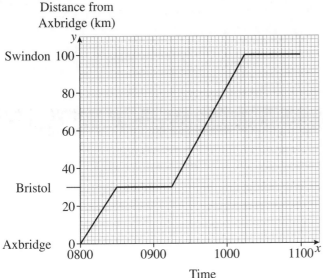

Distance from
Axbridge (km)

The graph shows the journey of a car from Axbridge to Swindon
via Bristol. The vertical axis shows the distance of the car from
Axbridge between 0800 and 1100.

**a** How far was the car from Axbridge at 0815?

**b** For how long did the car stop at Bristol?

**c** Find the speed of the car (in km/h) between Axbridge and Bristol.

**d** Find the speed of the car (in km/h) between Bristol and Swindon.

**2** The graph opposite shows a car
journey from Manchester.

**a** How far from Manchester is the
car at 1030?

**b** When is the car half way between
B and C?

**c** At what time is the car 30 km from
Manchester?

**d** Find the speed (in km/h) of the car
from B to C.

**e** Find the speed (in km/h) of the car
from C to D.

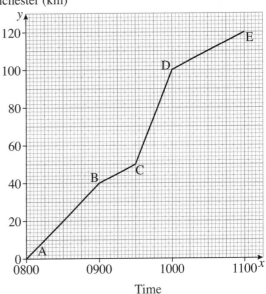

Distance from
Manchester (km)

**3** Copy these axes and sketch the graph of a car travelling at a steady speed then accelerating rapidly.

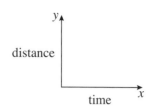

# STATISTICS 1                                        8

**1** For each statement below, write down whether it is:

impossible     unlikely     even chance     likely     certain

  **a** It will snow in January.

  **b** The next baby born will be a girl.

  **c** You will go to the toilet within the next week.

  **d** A friend will give you £10 000 within the next hour.

  **e** You will get 'heads' if you toss a coin.

**2** **a** Copy this *probability scale*.

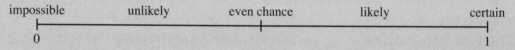

Use an arrow to place each event below on your probability scale:

  **b** You get a 5 if you roll a dice.

  **c** It will be the weekend within the next 7 days.

  **d** You will get a red card if you take one card from a pack of playing cards (26 cards out of 52 are red in a full pack).

  **e** You will wake up in Mexico tomorrow morning.

  **f** You will eat during the next 24 hours.

**1** Sandeep throws a dice 180 times. The dice lands 72 times on a '2'.

  **a** How many times should the dice land on a '2' if the dice is fair?

  **b** From Sandeep's results, find the *relative frequency* of getting a '2'.

$$\left(\text{relative frequency} = \frac{\text{number of times event happens}}{\text{total number of trials}}\right)$$

  **c** Do you think the dice is fair? *Explain* the answer you give.

**2** Freddie throws a coin 120 times. The coin lands on 'tails' 58 times.

   **a** From Freddie's results, find the relative frequency of getting 'tails'.

   **b** Do you think the coin is fair? *Explain* the answer you give.

**3** Jo is throwing an 8-sided dice. She throws the dice 240 times.
The table below shows her results.

| Score | 1 | 2 | 3 | 4 | 5 | 6 | 7 | 8 |
|---|---|---|---|---|---|---|---|---|
| Frequency | 27 | 24 | 36 | 27 | 30 | 27 | 33 | 36 |

   **a** How many times should each number come up if the dice is fair?

   **b** From Jo's results, *use a calculator* to find the relative frequency of getting each score
   (1 up to 8).

   **c** Do you think the dice is fair? *Explain* the answer you give.

---

**TASK M8.3** ——————————————————— **Main Book Page 246**

**1** Sue has 15 cards as shown below:

### T E L E V I S I O N C A L L S

Sue picks a card at random.
What is the probability that she picks the letter:

   **a** C          **b** E          **c** L          **d** S

**2** Angus has a bag which contains 7 toffees, 4 mints and 2 chocolates.
Angus picks one of these sweets.
What is the probability that he chooses a:

   **a** mint          **b** mint or toffee          **c** mint or chocolate

**3** A bag contains 10 beads. There are 6 blue,
3 red and 1 green.

   **a** Find the probability of selecting a red bead.

   **b** 2 more blue beads are put in the bag.
   Find the probability of selecting a blue bead.

**4** 24 people come for a job interview. 9 of these people wear glasses and 4 of them have
contact lenses.
Find the probability that the person chosen for the job:

   **a** has contact lenses

   **b** wears glasses

   **c** does not wear glasses or contact lenses.

**5** Wendy has six £5 notes, ten £10 notes and four £20 notes in her purse.
If she take out one note, what is the probability that it will be:

**a** a £20 note      **b** a £5 or £10 note      **c** a £50 note

**d** She buys a new toaster with a £20 note and a £10 note.
If she now took out a note, what is the probability that it would be a £10 note?

---

**TASK E8.1** ──────────────────────────────────── | **Main Book Page 248** |

**1** A coin is thrown 48 times. How many times would you expect it to land on 'heads'?

**2** A dice is thrown 120 times.
How many times would you expect to get a:

**a** 3          **b** 5          **c** 4 or 5          **d** square number

**3** This spinner is spun 80 times.
How many times should the spinner land on a '0'?

**4** The probability of Canning Albion winning a football match is $\frac{2}{3}$.
If they play 42 matches in a season, how many matches are they likely to win?

**5** The probability of Rob going to the pub on any one day is $\frac{2}{7}$.
How many times is he likely to go to the pub in the next fortnight?

**6** A bag contains 5 blue balls, 4 red balls and 1 yellow ball.
Brenda takes out one ball at random and then puts
it back. If she does this 70 times, how many times
would she take out:

**a** a yellow ball

**b** a blue ball

**c** a blue or red ball.

**7** A bag has only red and blue discs in it. The probability of picking red is $\frac{2}{5}$.

**a** What is the probability of picking a blue disc?

**b** Sam picks out 4 red discs without replacing them. What is the smallest number of blue discs
that could have been in the bag?

**c** If Sam picks out a total of 5 red discs without replacing them, what is the smallest number
of blue discs that could have been in the bag?

**8** In an animal rescue centre, the ratio of dogs to cats is $9:4$. There are 20 cats.
5 dogs leave the centre.
If one animal is chosen from the remaining dogs and cats, what is the probability that the chosen animal is a dog?

---

**TASK M8.4** ———————————————————— **Main Book Page 251**

**1** At a café, each person has a main course and a pudding.
One lunchtime the menu is:

      main course: Cottage pie or Macaroni cheese
      pudding: Trifle or Apple pie

List *all* the different meals that could be ordered.

**2** Here are 2 spinners. If I spin both spinners,
I could get a '1' and a '4' (1, 4)

   **a** List *all* the possible outcomes.

   **b** How many possible outcomes are there?

**3**  **a** Three babies are born. List *all* the boy/girl mixes
     (example: B G B  boy, girl, boy).

   **b** What is the probability of getting 2 girls and 1 boy (in any order)?

**4** Bart has 4 films (*Antz*, *King Kong*, *Jungle Book* and The *Terminator*).
He only has time to watch two of the films. List *all* the possible pairs of films that he could watch.

**5** Nina has 2 spinners. She spins both spinners
and multiplies the numbers.
For example a '3' and a '4' give 12.

   **a** Copy and complete this grid to show *all*
     the possible outcomes.

   **b** Find the probability of getting an answer
     of 4 when the 2 numbers are multiplied
     together.

| × | 1 | 2 | 3 | 4 |
|---|---|---|---|---|
| 1 | | | | |
| 2 | | | | |
| 3 | | | | 12 |
| 4 | | | | |

**1** 37 out of 60 people swim each week.
20 of the people who swim also go to the gym each week.
29 out of the 60 people go to the gym each week.

**a** Copy and complete the frequency tree below.

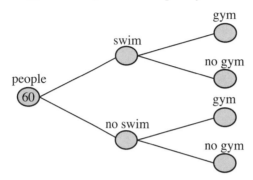

**b** If a person is chosen at random from those who swim, what is the probability that this person does not go to the gym each week?

**c** If a person is chosen at random from those who do not swim, what is the probability that this person goes to the gym each week?

**2** 58 out of 96 students achieve a grade 4 for their GCSE English.
46 of these 58 students also achieve a grade 4 in their GCSE Maths.
In total 71 students obtain a grade 4 in their GCSE Maths.

**a** Copy and complete the frequency tree below.

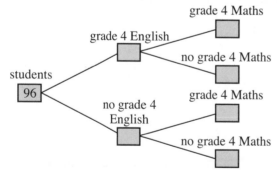

**b** If a student is chosen at random, what is the probability that the student did not obtain a grade 4 for English.

**c** If a student is chosen at random from those who did not attain a grade 4 for English, what is the probability that this student did not attain a grade 4 for Maths?

**3** Out of every 800 people given a dental check-up, 460 have no further treatment.
275 of the remaining people have a filling because they have tooth decay.
In total, 335 of the 800 people actually have tooth decay.

**a** Draw a frequency tree to show the above information.

**b** A person is chosen at random from those who have no further treatment.
What is the probability that this person has no tooth decay?

**4**

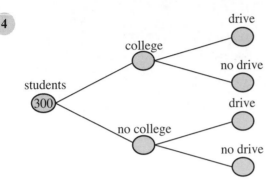

55% of 300 students go to college. Out of the students who do not go to college, 20% of them can drive. 30% of all the students can drive.

**a** Copy and complete the frequency tree.

**b** If one person is chosen at random from the students who go to college, what is the probability that this person does not drive?

---

**TASK M8.6** ———————————————————— **Main Book Page 255**

**1** The probability of a bus being late is $0.2$. What is the probability of the bus *not* being late?

**2** The probability of Sean getting up before 11 a.m. on a Saturday morning is $\frac{1}{4}$.
What is the probability of Sean *not* getting up before 11 a.m. on a
Saturday morning?

**3** The probability of Karen playing certain sports is shown in the table below.

| Hockey | Football | Badminton | Netball |
|--------|----------|-----------|---------|
| 0·5 | 0·1 | $x$ | 0·2 |

**a** What is the probability of Karen playing hockey or netball?

**b** What is the probability of Karen playing badminton?

**4** The probability of picking a picture card from a pack of cards is $\frac{3}{13}$.
What is the probability of *not* picking a picture card?

**5** If the probability of England winning the next football World Cup is $0.15$,
what is the probability of England *not* winning the next World Cup?

**6** Don gets to work by either car, bus, tube or bike.
The table shows the probabiity of each being used.

| Car | Bus | Tube | Bike |
|------|------|------|------|
| 0·25 | | 0·4 | 0·2 |

  **a** What is the probability of Don going to work by bus?

  **b** What is the probability of Don going to work by car or bus?

  **c** On his 20 working days in March, how many days would you expect Don to take the tube?

---

**TASK M8.7** ——————————————————— **Main Book Page 259**

**1** The Venn diagram shows students in Year 10 in a school ($\mathcal{E}$).

G = {students who study geography}
H = {students who study history}

  **a** How many students study history?

  **b** How many students are in Year 10?

  **c** How many students do not study geography or history?

$\mathcal{E}$, G 47 (64) 68 H 28

**2** $\mathcal{E}$ = {cars in a garage}
R = {red cars}
W = {cars with electric windows}

How many cars

  **a** have electric windows?

  **b** are not red?

  **c** are red and have electric windows?

  **d** are red?

$\mathcal{E}$, R 8 (14) 21 W 32

**3** 

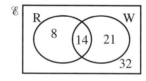

$\mathcal{E}$ = {people on a bus}
U = {people under 25 years old}
B = {people with blonde hair}

There are 33 people on the bus.
10 people have blonde hair and 11 people are under 25 years old.

  **a** Copy and complete the Venn diagram.

  **b** How many people are not under 25 years old and do not have blonde hair?

**4** 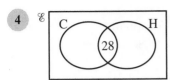 152 people walk down a street on a rainy day.
C = {people who wear a coat}
H = {people who wear a hat}

77 people wear a coat. 43 people do not wear a coat or a hat.

**a** Copy and complete the Venn diagram.

**b** How many people wear a hat but no coat?

---

**TASK M8.8** ──────────────────────────────── **Main Book Page 261**

**1** $\mathcal{E}$ = {people who play sport}
F = {people who play football}
R = {people who play rugby}

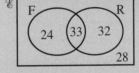

If one person is chosen at random then find

**a** the probability that the person plays football, i.e. $p$(football)

**b** $p$(plays rugby but not football)

**c** $p$(plays no rugby or football)

**2** $\mathcal{E}$ = {people at a dance class}
F = {females}
U = {under 25 years old}

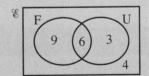

If one person is chosen at random then find

**a** $p$(female not under 25)

**b** $p$(male under 25)

**c** $p$(male not under 25)

**3** The Venn diagram opposite shows
a selection of numbers.

S = {square numbers}
C = {cube numbers}

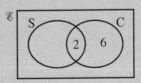

There are 11 square numbers which are not cube numbers.
There are 38 numbers in total.
If a number is chosen at random then find

**a** $p$(cube number)

**b** $p$(not a square number or a cube number)

**c** $p$(not a square number)

**4**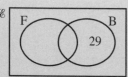

The Venn diagram opposite shows 85 play titles and whether they were films or books also.

F = {film titles}

B = {book titles}

There are 40 film titles and 47 book titles.
If one title is chosen at random, find

**a** $p$(a film and a book title)

**b** $p$(not a film or a book title)

**5**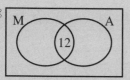

The Venn diagram opposite shows 185 students from Year 11 in a local school.

M = {students who study music}

B = {students who study art}

37 students study music. 75 students do not study music or art.
If a student is chosen at random, find

**a** $p$(studies art)

**b** $p$(does not study music)

**c** $p$(studies music but not art)

# GEOMETRY 2       9

**TASK M9.1** ———————————————— **Main Book Page 270**

Write down the time shown by each clock below:

**1**

**2**

**3**

**4**

**5**

**6**

**7** Write down the measurement indicated by each arrow.

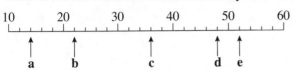

f  Write down the difference between **d** and **b**.

g  Write down the difference between **e** and **a**.

**8** Write down the measurement shown by each arrow below.

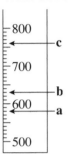

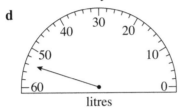

litres

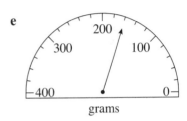

grams

---

**TASK M9.2** ———————————————————————— **Main Book Page 272**

**1** Write down the measurement indicated by each arrow.

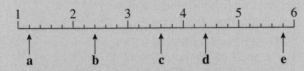

f  Write down the difference between **d** and **a**.

g  Write down the difference between **e** and **b**.

**2** Write down the measurement shown by each arrow below.

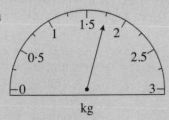

kg

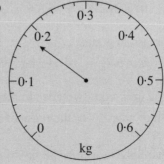

kg

c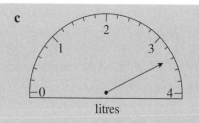
litres

d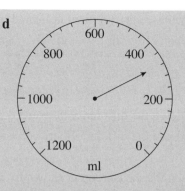
ml

3   Write down the measurement shown by each arrow below.

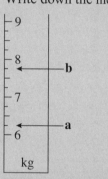
kg

litres

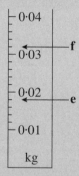
kg

4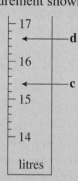

This is a fuel gauge on a car.
It is full with 56 litres of petrol.
Half an hour after the fuel gauge
looked like this, the driver had
used up another 6 litres of petrol.
How many litres of petrol were
now left in the car?

---

**TASK M9.3** ————————————————————————— **Main Book Page 273**

1   Write each length in cm.

   a  3 m       b  1·2 m      c  5·8 m      d  3·64 m      e  0·7 m

2   Write each mass in grams.

   a  4 kg      b  6·5 kg     c  3·2 kg     d  4·718 kg    e  0·9 kg

3   Which metric unit would you use to measure:

   a  the length of a car     b  the mass of a car     c  the width of a pin

4   Sam says that his dad weighs about 80 grams. Is this likely to
    be a good estimate?

> **Remember:**
> 10 mm = 1 cm
> 100 cm = 1 m
> 1000 m = 1 km
> 1000 g = 1 kg
> 1000 kg = 1 tonne
> 1000 mg = 1 gram
> 1000 ml = 1 litre
> 1 ml = 1 cm³
> 100 cl = 1 litre

5  Write each length in metres.

   **a** 600 cm     **b** 450 cm     **c** 5 km     **d** 5·3 km     **e** 7·186 km

6  Write each quantity in ml.

   **a** 8 litres   **b** 9·5 litres   **c** 4·6 litres   **d** 4·315 litres   **e** 60 cm³

7  Venkata has a 1 litre bottle of lemonade. If 560 ml of lemonade is
   used, how much is left in the bottle?

8  Toby is running in a 3 km race. He has covered 900 metres. How much
   further to the end of the race?

---

**TASK M9.4** ──────────────────────────────────── **Main Book Page 275**

1  Barry buys a 2·5 kg bag of potatoes. If he uses up 820 g of
   potatoes, what weight is left in the bag?

2  Beth walks 3·8 km and Simone walks 937 m. How much further
   has Beth walked than Simone.

3  Copy and complete the following:

   **a** 2·6 m = ☐ cm          **b** 3·82 m = ☐ cm          **c** 470 cm = ☐ m

   **d** 90 mm = ☐ cm          **e** 4 mm = ☐ cm            **f** 1500 m = ☐ km

   **g** 3·5 kg = ☐ g          **h** 600 g = ☐ kg           **i** 0·28 kg = ☐ g

   **j** 1·9 tonnes = ☐ kg     **k** 620 ml = ☐ litres      **l** 1937 litres = ☐ ml

   **m** 8·2 litres = ☐ ml     **n** 3·26 litres = ☐ ml     **o** 43 g = ☐ kg

4  A shop uses 40 g of cheese in one sandwich. How many sandwiches
   will the shop make if it has 3·2 kg of cheese?

5  Write the following amounts in order of size, starting with the smallest.

   **a** 8 cm, 0·81 m, 7·4 cm, 83 mm

   **b** 780 g, 0·7 kg, 738 g, 0·79 kg

   **c** 5 km, 57 m, 509 m, 0·6 km, 4·7 km

   **d** 274 ml, 0·28 l, 0·279 l, 275 ml, 2·14 l

---

**TASK M9.5** ──────────────────────────────────── **Main Book Page 276**

1  For each statement below, write true or false:

   **a** 8:30 p.m. = 20:30          **b** 4.30 a.m. = 16:30

   **c** 2:15 a.m. = 02:15          **d** 3:42 a.m. = 03:42

   **e** 10:50 p.m. = 10:50         **f** 5:17 p.m. = 17:17

**2** Sunil watches a 2 hour 15 minute film which starts at 7:50 p.m.
At what time does the film end?

**3** Patsy flies to Rome and arrives at 13:35. If the flight lasted for 2 hours 45 minutes,
when did the flight begin?

**4** Gabby borrows some money and has to pay it back within 5 years.
How many months does she have to pay back the money?

**5** Gareth wakes up at the time shown on the clock.
He has to be at work by 9 a.m. How long has he
got before he must be at work?

**6** André needs to be at Waterloo station by 5:30 p.m. A train leaves his
home town at 15:48 and takes 1 hour 40 minutes to get to Waterloo
station. Will he arrive at Waterloo station in time?

**7** Copy and complete this bus timetable. Each bus takes the same time
between stops.

|  | Bus 1 | Bus 2 | Bus 3 | Bus 4 | Bus 5 |
|---|---|---|---|---|---|
| **Bus Station** | 07:50 | 08:35 | 08:55 | 09:45 | 10:25 |
| **Cinema** | 07:59 |  |  |  |  |
| **Town Hall** | 08:10 |  |  |  |  |
| **Cherry Hill** | 08:22 |  | 09:27 |  |  |
| **Train Station** | 08:35 |  |  | 10:30 |  |

---

**TASK M9.6** ———————————————————— **Main Book Page 278**

Use $\triangle$ to help you work out the questions below:

**1** Find the speed for each distance and time shown below.
  **a** distance = 60 miles, time = 3 hours
  **b** distance = 325 km, time = 5 hours

**2** Find the distance for each speed and time shown below.
  **a** speed = 45 mph, time = 2 hours
  **b** speed = 58 mph, time = $\frac{1}{2}$ hour

**3** Find the time taken for each distance and speed shown below.

   **a** distance = 280 km, speed = 70 km/hr

   **b** distance = 50 km, speed = 20 km/hr

**4** Copy and complete this table.

| Distance (km) | Time (hours) | Speed (km/hr) |
|---|---|---|
| 324 | 9 | |
| | 4 | 51 |
| | 1·5 | 60 |
| 150 | | 25 |
| 245 | | 35 |
| 40 | 0·5 | |

**5** Jack cycles 3 km in 15 minutes. What was his average speed in km/hr?

**6** Brenda drives from Nottingham to Leeds at an average speed of 84 km/hr. The journey takes 1 hour 30 minutes. How far is it from Nottingham to Leeds?

---

**TASK E9.1**                                                  **Main Book Page 279**

**1** Find the speed in mph for each of the following.

| Distance | Time | Speed (mph) |
|---|---|---|
| 13 miles | 15 minutes | |
| 7 miles | 10 minutes | |
| 4 miles | 5 minutes | |
| 30 miles | 20 minutes | |
| 17 miles | 12 minutes | |

**2** A train travels 47 km in 20 minutes. What is the speed of the train in km/hr?

**3** Ellen drives 24 km from her home to work. She travels at an average speed of 32 km/hr. If she leaves home at 8:05 a.m., when will she arrive at work?

**4** Jane travels at 12 km/hr for 1 hour 15 minutes and Pete travels at 6 km/hr for 2 hours 30 minutes.
Who travels further and by how much?

**5** Change the following speeds into the units indicated.

    **a** 18 km/h into m/s           **b** 72 km/h into m/s

    **c** 15 m/s into km/h           **d** 35 m/s into km/h

**6** Li travels 150 m in 15 seconds. What is his speed in km/h?

**7** A missile travels at 110 m/s. How long will it take to travel 594 km?

**8** Alexa travels at 108 km/h. How far does she travel in half a minute?
Give the answer in metres.

---

**TASK M9.7**                                  **Main Book Page 281**

**1** For each shape below you are given the perimeter. Find the missing value $x$.
All lengths are in cm.

    **a**                   **b**                   **c**

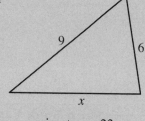

perimeter = 23 cm          perimeter = 35 cm         perimeter = 30 cm

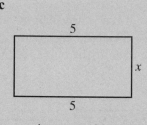

**2** Draw 3 different rectangles with a perimeter of 14 cm.

**3** The perimeter of these two rectangles is the same. Find the missing value $x$.

**4** All lengths are in cm.

    **a** Find the length of $a$ and $b$.

    **b** Find the perimeter of this shape.

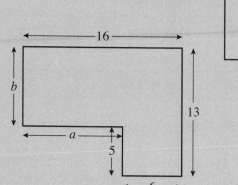

In questions ⑤ to ⑦, find the perimeter of each shape. All lengths are in cm.

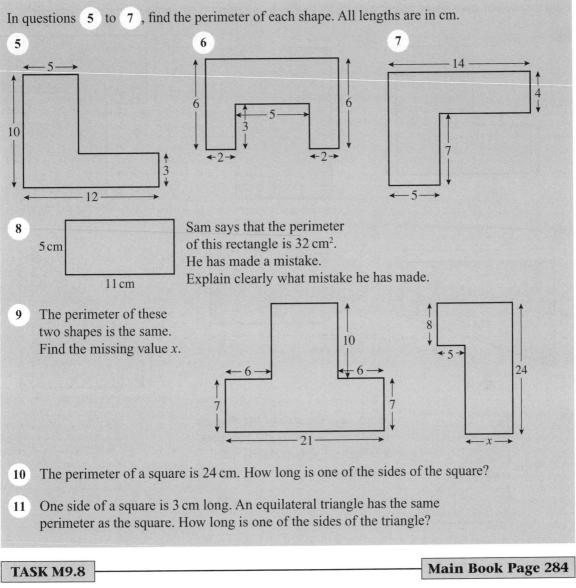

**8** Sam says that the perimeter of this rectangle is 32 cm². He has made a mistake. Explain clearly what mistake he has made.

**9** The perimeter of these two shapes is the same. Find the missing value *x*.

**10** The perimeter of a square is 24 cm. How long is one of the sides of the square?

**11** One side of a square is 3 cm long. An equilateral triangle has the same perimeter as the square. How long is one of the sides of the triangle?

---

**TASK M9.8** ————————————————— **Main Book Page 284**

**1** The perimeter of this triangle is 24 cm. Work out the area of the triangle.

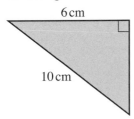

**2** Find the value of *x*.

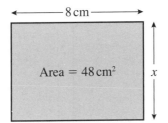

Find the area of each shape in questions **3** to **8** by splitting them into rectangles or triangles.

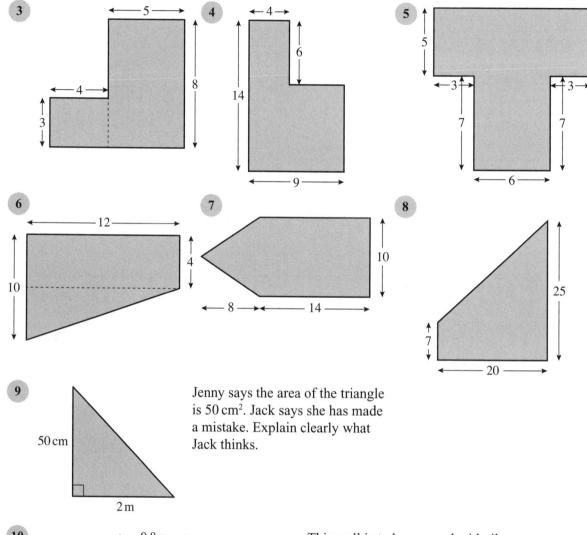

**9**

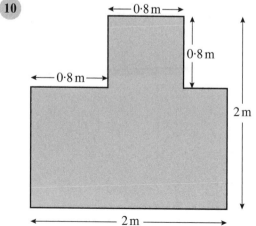

Jenny says the area of the triangle is 50 cm². Jack says she has made a mistake. Explain clearly what Jack thinks.

**10**

This wall is to be covered with tiles.
Each tile is 20 cm by 20 cm.
The tiles are sold in boxes of 10.
Each box costs £22·90.
Work out the least amount of money needed to buy enough tiles.

**TASK M9.9** ——————————————————— **Main Book Page 287**

Find the area of each shape below. All lengths are in cm.

**1**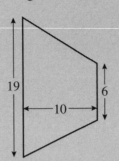

**2**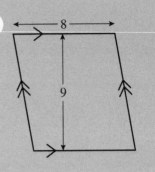

**3**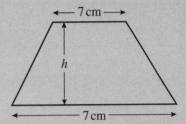

**4** The area of this trapezium is 8 cm². What is the value of $h$?

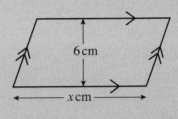

**5** The area of the parallelogram is equal to the area of the trapezium. Find the value of $x$.

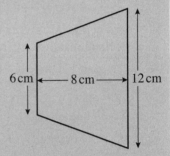

**6** Work out the ratio of the area of shape P to the area of shape Q.

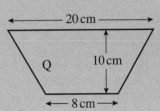

**7** Work out the area of this parallelogram.

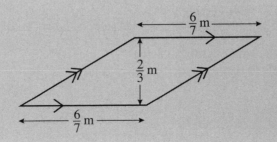

**8** Find the shaded area.

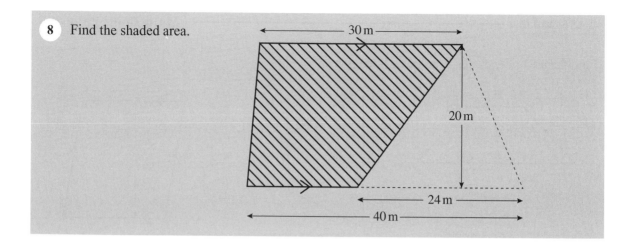

---

**1** What is the radius of a circle if the diameter is 46 cm?

**2** What is the diameter of a circle if the radius is 19 mm?

**3** *Use a calculator* to find the circumference of each circle below (give answers to 1 decimal place).

**a** 12 cm     **b** 3 m     **c** 9 cm     **d** 17 m

**4** Jed bakes a cake in a circular tin of diameter 25 cm. He has a 75 cm long piece of ribbon which he wants to wrap around the circumference of the cake.
Is the ribbon long enough?
*Explain* your answer fully.

**5** Which shape has the larger perimeter – the triangle or the circle? Show all your working out.

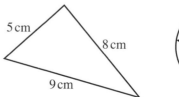

**6** Which circle has the larger perimeter?
Show all your working out.

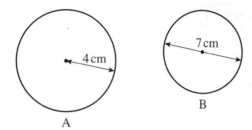

A

B

---

**TASK E9.2** ──────────────────────────── **Main Book Page 291**

Calculate the perimeter of each shape. All arcs are either semi-circles or quarter circles. Give answers correct to 1 decimal place.

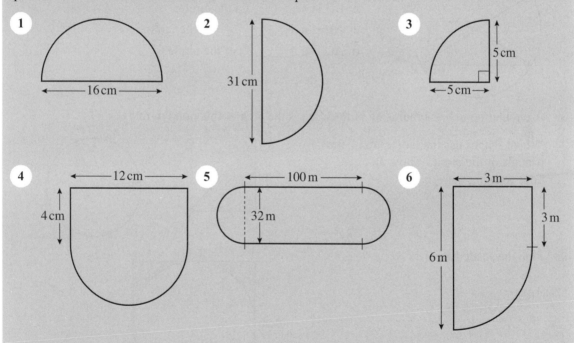

**7** A circular log of diameter 30 cm is rolled down a hill. It rolls 48 metres. How many *complete* revolutions did the log make before it stopped?

**8** Maisy has a bike with wheels of radius 31·5 cm. She cycles 3 km. How many times do the wheels of her bike go round completely?

**9** A golf ball is rolled 3·6 m across a putting green and drops into the hole. How many complete revolutions does the ball make before it drops into the hole if the ball's diameter is 4 cm?

H/W

**TASK M9.10** ———————————————————— **Main Book Page 293**

Calculate the area of each circle below, correct to 1 decimal place.

**1**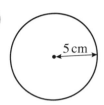
5 cm

**2**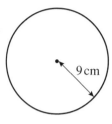
9 cm

**3**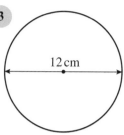
12 cm

**4**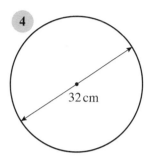
32 cm

**5**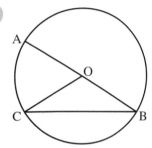

Copy and complete each sentence below:

**a** OC is a r _ _ _ _ _ of the circle.

**b** BC is a c _ _ _ _ in the circle.

**c** AB is a d _ _ _ _ _ _ of the circle.

**d** AO is a r _ _ _ _ _ of the circle.

**6** A circular pond has a radius of 11 m. What is the area of this pond in m²?

**7** Which shapes has the larger area – the triangle or the circle? Show all your working out.

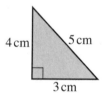
4 cm  5 cm  3 cm

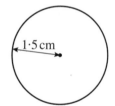
1·5 cm

**8** Find the shaded area.

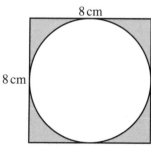
8 cm
8 cm

**9** Do *not* use a calculator in this question.
Find the area of each circle, leaving $\pi$ in your answer (for example, $16\pi$).

**a**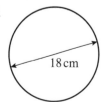
18 cm

**b**
4 cm

**c**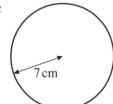
7 cm

In questions **1** to **3** find the area of each shape. All arcs are either semi-circles or quarter circles and the units are cm. Give answers correct to 1 decimal place.

**1**
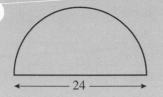

**2**
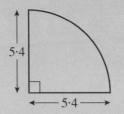

**3**
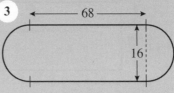

**4**
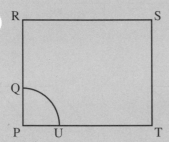

The area of square PRST is 36 cm².
PQ : QR = 1 : 2 and PU : UT = 1 : 2
Calculate the area of the quarter circle PQU.

In questions **5** to **7** find the shaded area. Lengths are in cm.
Give answers correct to 1 decimal place.

**5**
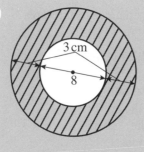

**6**
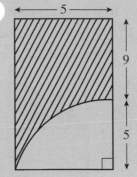

**7**
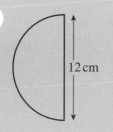

**8**  A circular pond has a radius of 13 m. A path goes all the way round the circumference of the pond. The path is 1·2 m wide throughout. Find the area of the path.

**9**
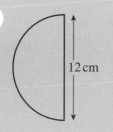

Find the area of this semi-circle, leaving $\pi$ in your answer (for example, $10\pi$).

114

**1** Copy and complete the table below to find the total surface area of the cuboid.

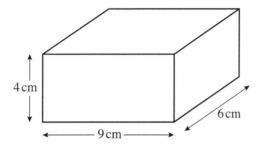

| face | area (cm²) |
|---|---|
| front | |
| back | |
| top | |
| bottom | |
| side 1 | |
| side 2 | |
| Total = | |

**2** Find the volume in cm³ of the cuboid in question **1** .

**3**

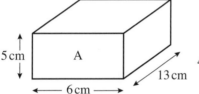 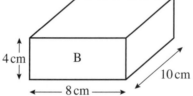 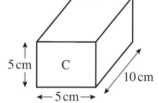

**a** Which of these 3 cuboids has the largest surface area?

**b** What is the *difference* between the largest surface area and the smallest surface area?

**c** Which of the cuboids has the smallest volume?

**d** What is the *difference* between the largest volume and the smallest volume?

**4**

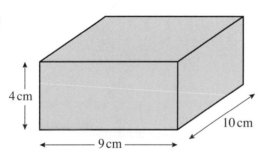

Write down the ratio of the area of the cuboid front face to the area of the top face. Give the answer in its simplest form.

**5** Laura says the volume of the cube opposite is 64 cm. Explain why her answer is not valid.

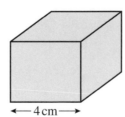

**6** 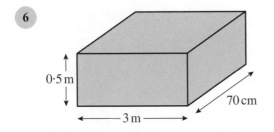 Work out the volume of this cuboid.

0·5 m   70 cm   3 m

---

**TASK M9.12** ——————————— **Main Book Page 298**

Find the volume of each prism below:

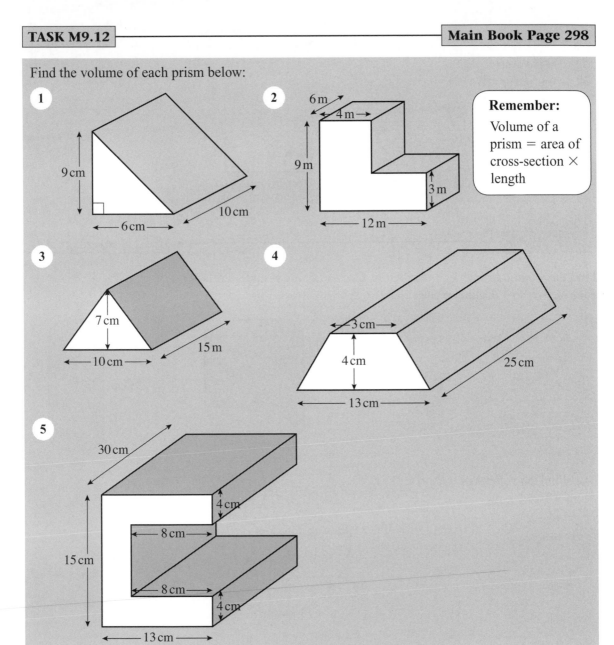

**1**

9 cm
6 cm
10 cm

**2**

6 m
4 m
9 m
3 m
12 m

**Remember:**

Volume of a prism = area of cross-section × length

**3**

7 cm
10 cm
15 m

**4**

3 cm
4 cm
13 cm
25 cm

**5**

30 cm
4 cm
8 cm
15 cm
8 cm
4 cm
13 cm

**6** The volume of a prism is 296 cm³. If the length of the prism is 8 cm, what is its cross-sectional area?

**7**

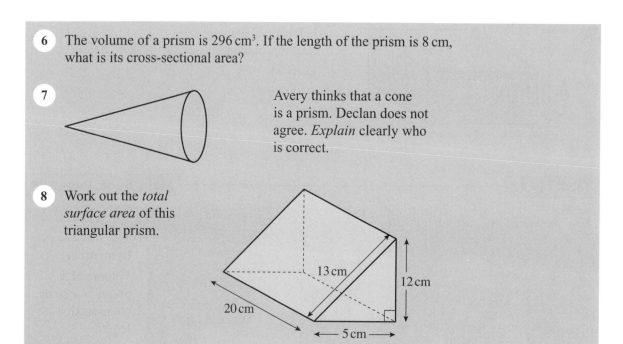

Avery thinks that a cone is a prism. Declan does not agree. *Explain* clearly who is correct.

**8** Work out the *total surface area* of this triangular prism.

13 cm

12 cm

20 cm

5 cm

---

**TASK M9.13**          **Main Book Page 301**

Find the volume of each cylinder below. *Use a calculator* and give each answer to 1 decimal place.

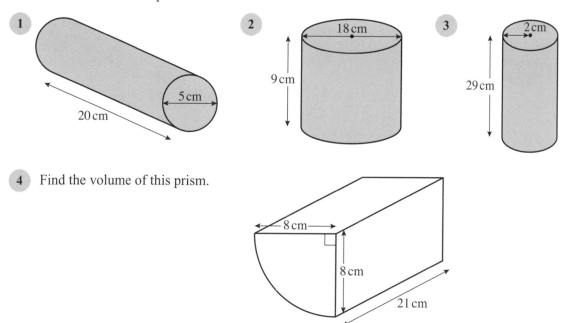

**1** 20 cm, 5 cm

**2** 18 cm, 9 cm

**3** 2 cm, 29 cm

**4** Find the volume of this prism.

8 cm

8 cm

21 cm

**5**

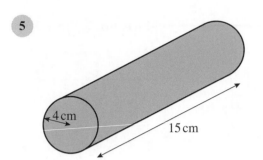

4 cm

15 cm

Find the volume of this cylinder, leaving $\pi$ in your answer (for example, $28\pi$).

**6** A pipe of diameter 8 cm and length 3 m is half full of water. How many litres of water are in the pipe?

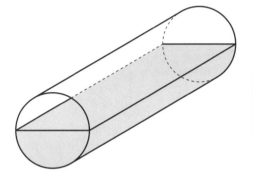

**Remember:**
$1 \text{ m}^3 = 1000$ litres
and change 8 cm
into metres

**7** The cylindrical tank opposite is filled with oil at a rate of 0·4 litres per second.
How long does it take to fill the tank completely?

**a** Give the answer to the nearest second.

**b** Give the answer to the nearest minute.

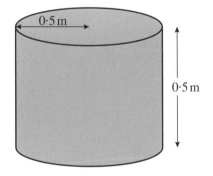

0·5 m

0·5 m

**8** A cylindrical bucket has a diameter of 30 cm and a height of 35 cm.
How many full bucket loads of water are needed to fill up the tank opposite.

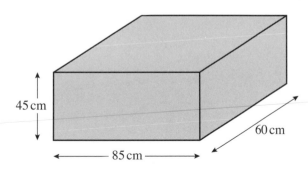

45 cm

60 cm

85 cm

118

**1**  *Explain* why these triangles are similar.

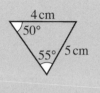
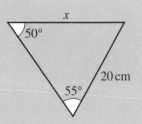

**2**  Which triangles below are similar to triangle P?

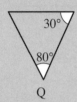

**3**

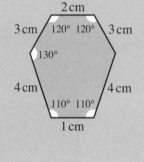

Explain clearly why
the 2 shapes opposite
are similar.

**4**  Find *y*.

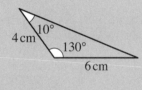
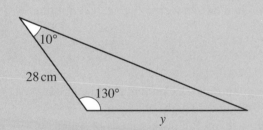

**5**

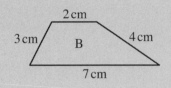

Explain clearly
why shapes
A and B are
not similar.

**6** For each part of the question below, the shapes are similar. Find $x$.

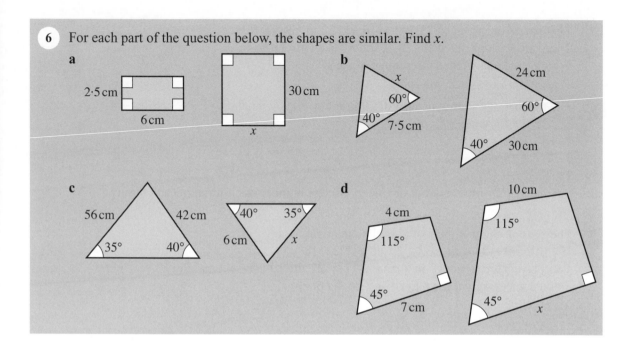

a

b

c

d

# STATISTICS 2                                                    10

**TASK M10.1**                                    **Main Book Page 314**

**1** Write the following numbers in order of size then write down the median.

7   2   18   4   6   14   12   19   14

**2** Find the mode of each set of numbers below:

**a**   3   7   1   4   5   3   5   2   3   4   9   3   6

**b**   5   4   6   2   4   6   1   6   2   8   3   2

**3** 10 people weigh the following (in kg):

65   85   70   65   80   95   70   85   90   95

Find their mean average weight.

For each set of numbers below, find

**a** the mean          **b** the median          **c** the mode          **d** the range.

**4**   6   10   9   3   16   10   2

**5**   8   11   4   8   15   4   16   5   10

**6**   6   3   9   9   2   7

**7** There are 5 people aged 23, 48, 46, 9 and 58 in a Rolls Royce.
There are 4 people aged 57, 28, 4 and 31 in a Citroen Saxo.
Which car contains the larger range of ages?

**8** The number of children in each of 20 families is shown below:

```
2  3  0  1  4
1  2  1  2  0
3  2  2  1  5
2  1  2  0  2
```

*Use a calculator* to work out the mean average number of children in each family.

**9** The ages of the members of a football team are:

```
19  27  22  21  24  33  29  26  22  18  31
```

Two players are 'sent off' in a match. They are the 29 year-old and the 18 year-old.
Find the mean age of the players left on the pitch.

---

**TASK E10.1** ──────────────────────────────────── **Main Book Page 316**

**1** Seven people score the following marks in a test:

```
30  40  40  40  45  45  96
```

Find
**a** the mean
**b** the median
**c** Which average best describes these marks? *Explain why.*

**2** In a shooting match, Rose scores:

8, 9, 9, 9, 10, 9, 9, 9, 9, 10

Find
**a** the mode
**b** the mean
**c** Which average best describes these scores, the mode or the mean? *Explain why.*

**3** ☐ ☐ 4 ☐ ☐ 9 ☐ ☐

Ross has 5 cards.
The 5 cards have a mean of 7, a median of 7 and a range of 13.
What are the 5 numbers on the cards?

**4** Claire scores 62% in a maths exam which is the median mark in her class.
What percentage of the students in her class scored less than Claire in this maths exam?

**5** The mean average age of 6 people is 37.
What is the total of all their ages?

**6** The mean weight of 11 people is 63 kg.

 **a** What is the total weight of all 11 people?

 **b** One person of weight 83 kg leaves the group.
 Find the mean weight of the remaining 10 people.

**7** The mean average of the 8 numbers below is 7.
 Work out the value of *n*.

 | 9 | 1 | *n* | 6 | 6 | 8 | 11 | 5 |

**8** Which kind of average is the most sensible to use to show the amount of money earned by each person in the UK. *Explain why.*

**9** Five numbers have mean average 7. Their mode is 3. The median is 8.
 Write down the five possible numbers.

 | ? | ? | 8 | ? | ? |

**10** The mean average salary of 7 people is £26 500.
 Gemma joins the group. If she earns £32 100,
 what is the mean average salary of all 8 people?

---

**TASK M10.2**      **Main Book Page 319**

**1** The bar chart shows how many goals, Towton United and Hotley Albion, scored in each of the years shown.

How many goals did Towton United score in:

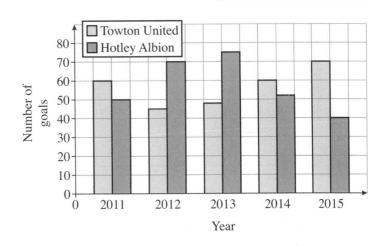

 **a** 2011

 **b** 2012

 **c** 2015

 **d** In which year did Hotley Albion score 76 goals?

 **e** In which years did Towton United score the same number of goals?

 **f** How many *more* goals did Hotley Albion score than Towton United in 2013?

 **g** How many *more* goals did Towton United score than Hotley Albion in 2015?

 **h** Which team scored more goals during *all* 5 years and how many more did they score?

**2** In an accident 'blackspot', there were 8 accidents in 2011, 10 accidents in 2012, 6 accidents in 2013, 14 accidents in 2014 and 4 accidents in 2015.

a Copy and complete the pictogram below:

| 2011 | |
|------|--|
| 2012 | |
| 2013 | ⊟ ⊢ |
| 2014 | |
| 2015 | |

⊟ means 4 accidents

b What fraction of the accidents in the pictogram took place in 2014?

**3** The graph below shows how many males and females work at an electronics firm called 'Manucomp'.

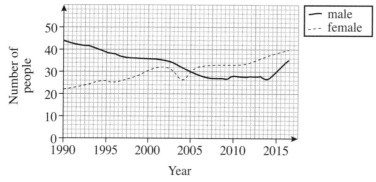

How many female workers were there in:

a 1995          b 2010          c 2015

d In what year were there the same number of male and female workers?

e How many *more* female workers than male workers were there in year 2010?

f What was the rise in female workers between 1990 and 2015?

---

**TASK M10.3** ──────────────────────────── **Main Book Page 322**

**1** This stem and leaf diagram shows how much money was raised by some children on a sponsored 'silence'.

a Write down the median amount of money.

b What is the range of these amounts of money?

| Stem | Leaf |
|------|------|
| 1 | 7 9 |
| 2 | 4 4 5 8 9 9 |
| 3 | 2 6 6 |
| 4 | 3 8 8 8 |
| 5 | 1 4 |

Key 2|4 = £24

**2** The weights of 22 people were recorded to the nearest kg.

64  71  63  78  82  49  71  65  74  78  53
58  82  66  65  71  87  65  53  72  68  81

**a** Show this data on an ordered stem and leaf diagram.

**b** Write down the range of this data.

**c** If one person is chosen at random, what is the probability that this person weighs more than 75 kg?

**d** What percentage of their weights were *between* 65 kg and 75 kg?
(Give the answer to 1 decimal place)

**3** The heights of the players in hockey teams, the Tampton Trojans and Mallow Town, are shown in the back-to-back stem and leaf diagram.

| The Tampton Trojans | | Mallow Town |
|---|---|---|
| | 15 | 6 |
| 9  3 | 16 | 1  8  8 |
| 8  5  5  2  1 | 17 | 2  4  7  7 |
| 4  4  3 | 18 | 3 |
| 6 | 19 | 0  2 |

Key 2|17 = 172     Key 18|3 = 183

**a** Find the median and range for Mallow Town.

**b** Find the median and range for the Tampton Trojans.

**c** Write a sentence to compare the heights of the players in each hockey team (use the median and range).

**TASK M10.4** — **Main Book Page 325**

**1** The table opposite shows how a group of people get to work each morning.

**a** Find the total frequency.

**b** Work out the angle for each person to help draw a pie chart. (i.e. 360° ÷ 'total frequency')

**c** Work out the angle for each type of transport and draw a pie chart.

| Type of transport | Frequency (number of people) |
|---|---|
| bus | 30 |
| car | 10 |
| tube | 25 |
| on foot | 15 |
| bike | 10 |

124

**2** James asks some people what their favourite type of film is. A tally chart of his findings is shown below.

| Film type | Tally |
|-----------|-------|
| adventure | ⅠⅠⅠⅠ Ⅰ |
| comedy | ⅠⅠⅠⅠ ⅠⅠⅠⅠ ⅠⅠⅠⅠ ⅠⅠⅠ |
| horror | ⅠⅠⅠⅠ ⅠⅠ |
| romance | ⅠⅠ |
| cartoon | ⅠⅠⅠⅠ ⅠⅠⅠⅠ ⅠⅠ |

Draw a pie chart to show these findings.

**3** Some people are asked what their favourite colour is. The information is shown in the table opposite. Draw a pie chart to display this information.

| Colour | Frequency |
|--------|-----------|
| blue | 23 |
| green | 8 |
| red | 28 |
| yellow | 41 |
| purple | 4 |
| other | 16 |

---

**TASK M10.5** Main Book Page 327

**1** 300 people were asked what their favourite hot drink is.
The pie chart shows the findings.
How many people chose:

  **a** coffee      **b** others      **c** tea

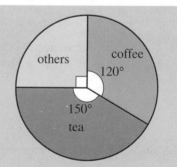

**2** 10,000 people were surveyed about which continent they would prefer to buy their car from.
The pie chart shows this information.
Find the angle on the pie chart for:

  **a** Europe      **b** Asia      **c** America

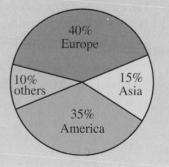

**3** This pie chart shows the favourite 'spirits' chosen
by some people.
240 people chose whiskey.
How many people chose:

   **a** vodka        **b** gin        **c** brandy

**4** The pie charts opposite show
the favourite sports of students
from Canning High School
and Henton Park School.

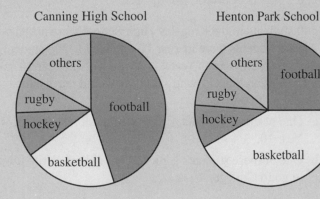

*Explain* why you *cannot* say that more students like football in Canning High School than
in Henton Park School.

---

| TASK M10.6 | Main Book Page 330 |

**1** 400 people were asked if they could drive or not.
The information is shown in the two-way table.

|  | **Drive** | **Not drive** | **Total** |
|---|---|---|---|
| Female | 110 |  | 170 |
| Male |  |  |  |
| Total | 290 |  | 400 |

   **a** Copy and complete the table.

   **b** How many males could not drive?

**2** 600 students were asked whether they preferred English, Maths or Science.
73 boys preferred Maths and 89 boys chose Science.
306 students chose English in total.
352 girls were asked.
How many girls chose English if 131 students chose Maths in total?

**3** Some people were asked if they would rather watch a film on a dvd,
at the cinema or go to the theatre.
The results are shown below:
M = Male, F = Female, d = dvd, c = cinema, t = theatre

| | | | | | |
|---|---|---|---|---|---|
| M, c | M, c | F, c | F, d | F, c | |
| F, d | F, t | F, d | M, t | M, c | |
| F, d | F, t | F, d | M, t | M, c | |
| F, d | F, t | F, d | M, t | M, c | |
| M, c | F, c | M, c | F, t | F, d | |
| F, d | F, d | M, t | M, d | F, c | |

**a** Put these results into a two-way table.

**b** What percentage of the males chose the theatre?

**4** 500 students in the Kingsley High School were asked what they planned to do after Year 11.
All the students were in Year 10 or Year 11. 206 students said they would stay in the 6th Form,
120 of whom were in Year 11. 26 students in Year 10 said they would leave education, 5 less
than those in Year 11 who said they would leave education. 109 students in Year 11 said they
would go to college.

**a** One of these students is picked at random. Write down the *probability* that the student is in
Year 10.

**b** One of these students is picked at random. Write down the *probability* that the student plans
to go to College.

---

**TASK M10.7** | **Main Book Page 333**

**1** Describe the correlation in this scatter graph.

**2** **a** Describe the correlation in this scatter graph.

**b** Suggest what X and Y might be to give this scatter graph.

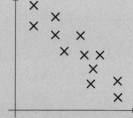

**3** The table below shows the English test results and heights of 16 students.

| Score (%) | 82 | 53 | 80 | 76 | 67 | 46 | 67 | 71 | 61 | 83 | 72 | 48 | 73 | 75 | 59 | 45 |
|---|---|---|---|---|---|---|---|---|---|---|---|---|---|---|---|---|
| Height (cm) | 175 | 182 | 193 | 160 | 168 | 165 | 183 | 197 | 159 | 163 | 175 | 161 | 164 | 188 | 170 | 193 |

a Copy and complete this scatter graph to show the data in the table about English test results and heights.

b Describe the correlation in this scatter graph.

c One of these students is picked at random. Write down the probability that the student scored *more* than 75% in the English test.

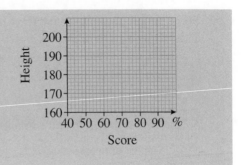

**TASK M10.8** ———————————————————— **Main Book Page 335**

**1** Lauren received £59 000 commission for selling last year.
Marcus received £31 000 commission for selling last year.
Lauren is a better salesperson.
Why might this be misleading? Discuss.

**2**

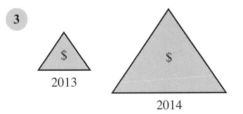

The bar chart opposite shows how many nails have been sold by 3 stores P, Q and R.
Why is this not a good representation?
Discuss.

**3**

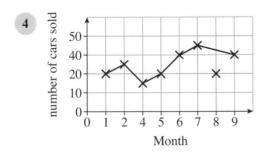

A firm's sales increased by 25% in 2014 compared to 2013.
Why is this diagram misleading?

**4**

The graph opposite shows how many cars are sold during a period of time.
Give at least two reasons why this graph is misleading.

**5**  Some people are asked what their favourite colour is.
The results are shown below.

| Colour | blue | red | yellow | green | pink |
|---|---|---|---|---|---|
| **Number of people** | 11 | 10 | 12 | 13 | 9 |

A bar chart is drawn to show this information.

Number of people

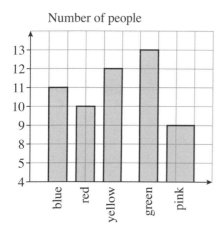

Write down all the mistakes that
have been made with this bar chart.

**6**  'Probably the best chocolate in the world' is stated in an advert for a chocolate company.
Why is this statement misleading? Discuss.

---

**TASK M10.9**                                                      **Main Book Page 337**

**1**  The table below shows the weights of some people.

| Weight (kg) | 60 | 61 | 62 | 63 |
|---|---|---|---|---|
| Frequency | 3 | 6 | 5 | 1 |

Find   **a**  the modal weight

       **b**  the median weight.

**2**  The table below shows the number of drinks some children had
during one day.

| Number of drinks | 1 | 2 | 3 | 4 | 5 |
|---|---|---|---|---|---|
| Frequency | 7 | 12 | 8 | 23 | 29 |

Find   **a**  the modal number of drinks

       **b**  the median number of drinks.

**3** The table opposite shows the neck sizes of a group of people.

Find **a** the modal interval

 **b** the interval which contains the median.

| Neck size (cm) | Frequency |
|---|---|
| 12 to 14 | 36 |
| $14\frac{1}{2}$ to $15\frac{1}{2}$ | 81 |
| 16 to $16\frac{1}{2}$ | 75 |
| 17 to $17\frac{1}{2}$ | 29 |
| over $17\frac{1}{2}$ | 14 |

**4** Some students from nearby schools are asked how often they go each month to a local skateboard park. The information is shown in the tables below.

| Chetley Park School | |
|---|---|
| Park visits | Frequency |
| 0 to 1 | 27 |
| 2 to 5 | 21 |
| 6 to 9 | 15 |
| 10 or more | 8 |

| Wetton School | |
|---|---|
| Park visits | Frequency |
| 0 to 1 | 19 |
| 2 to 5 | 23 |
| 6 to 9 | 34 |
| 10 or more | 17 |

**a** For each school, find the interval which contains the median.

**b** From which school do students generally go to the skateboard park more often? Explain why you think this.

---

**TASK M10.10** ──────────────────────────── **Main Book Page 339**

*Use a calculator if you need to.*

**1** Some young people were asked how many different mobile phones they had owned during the last 6 years. The information is shown in the table below.

| Number of phones | 0 | 1 | 2 | 3 | 4 |
|---|---|---|---|---|---|
| Frequency | 7 | 4 | 12 | 14 | 3 |

**a** Find the total number of phones.

**b** Find the mean average number of phones.

**2** Some people were asked how many computers they had in total in their houses.

| Number of computers | Frequency |
|---|---|
| 0 | 16 |
| 1 | 26 |
| 2 | 37 |
| 3 | 20 |
| 4 | 5 |

a Find the total number of computers.

b Find the mean average number of computers per house (give your answer to 1 decimal place).

**3** Some people are asked how often they go to the cinema during one month. Their responses are shown in the chart below.

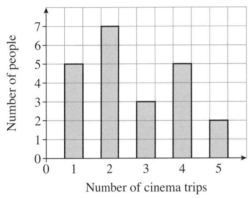

Number of cinema trips

a Work out the mean average number of cinema trips for this group of people.

b Which number of trips is the mode?

**TASK M10.11** ———————————— **Main Book Page 342**

**1** Some people were asked how many times they ate out in a restaurant or pub during one month. The information is shown below.

| Number of meals (m) | $0 \leqslant m \leqslant 1$ | $2 \leqslant m \leqslant 4$ | $5 \leqslant m \leqslant 9$ | $10 \leqslant m \leqslant 19$ |
|---|---|---|---|---|
| Frequency | 24 | 39 | 16 | 12 |

a Estimate the total number of meals.

b Estimate the mean average (give your answer to the nearest whole number).

c *Explain* why your answer is an estimate.

**2** The number of goals scored by two hockey teams over the last 15 years is shown in the tables below.

| Batton City | |
|---|---|
| Number of goals ($g$) | Frequency |
| $20 \leq g \leq 29$ | 2 |
| $30 \leq g \leq 39$ | 3 |
| $40 \leq g \leq 49$ | 5 |
| $50 \leq g \leq 59$ | 4 |
| $60 \leq g \leq 69$ | 1 |

| Chorley Town | |
|---|---|
| Number of goals ($g$) | Frequency |
| $20 \leq g \leq 29$ | 2 |
| $30 \leq g \leq 39$ | 6 |
| $40 \leq g \leq 49$ | 4 |
| $50 \leq g \leq 59$ | 3 |
| $60 \leq g \leq 69$ | 0 |

**a** Which team has scored the higher mean average number of goals?

**b** Write down the value of the higher mean average (give your answer to one decimal place).

**c** What is the *difference* between the mean average number of goals scored by each team?

---

**TASK M10.12/M10.13** ——————————————— **Main Book Page 344**

**1** The hourly rates of pay for 5 workers at a baker's shop are £5·30, £5·30, £6·80, £5·75 and £7·25.

The hourly rates of pay at a butcher's shop for 6 workers are £5·65, £6·75, £8·30, £5·90, £5·90 and £6.

Copy and complete the statements below to compare the pay rates of the 2 shops.

Baker's shop: median = £_____     range = £_____

Butcher's shop: median = £_____     range = £_____

'The median for the baker's shop is (*greater/smaller*) than the median for the butcher's shop. The range for the baker's shop is (*greater/smaller*) than the range for the butcher's shop (i.e. the pay rates for the baker's shop are (*more/less*) spread out).'

**2** Sam and Polly record the number of e-mails they receive each day during January. The information is shown below:

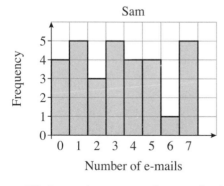

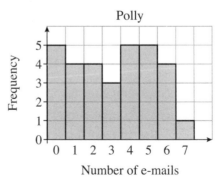

**a** Work out the mean and range for Sam.     **b** Work out the mean and range for Polly.

**c** Write a sentence to compare the number of e-mails received each day by Sam and Polly.

**3** The number of 'fizzy' drinks drunk each week by some children is shown below:

Class 8C  2  3  2  5  3  0  1  2  1  3  6  4  3  4
Class 8D  0  3  1  7  2  0  2  5  6  2  3  1  2

Copy and complete the statements below to compare the number of 'fizzy' drinks drunk by these children in class 8C and class 8D.

Class 8C: mode = _____   range = _____

Class 8D: mode = _____   range = _____

'The mode for class 8C is (*greater/smaller*) than the mode for class 8D and the range of class 8C is (*greater/smaller*) than the range of class 8D (i.e. the number of 'fizzy' drinks drunk in class 8C is (*more/less*) spread out).'

**4** The scatter graph below shows the ages of a make of car A and its value.

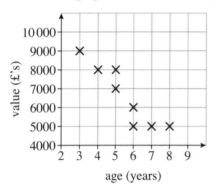

age (years)

Some other cars of a different make B have a mean value of £7350 and a range of £5400.

Write a statement to compare the value of car A with the value of car B.

**5** Some 8 year olds and some 18 year-olds are asked how many Christmas presents they had last Christmas.

| 8 year-olds | |
|---|---|
| 0 to 8 | 6 |
| 9 to 16 | 31 |
| 17 to 24 | 48 |
| 25 to 32 | 10 |
| 33 to 40 | 3 |
| 41 to 48 | 2 |

| 18 year-olds | |
|---|---|
| 0 to 8 | 34 |
| 9 to 16 | 26 |
| 17 to 24 | 9 |
| 25 to 32 | 5 |
| 33 to 40 | 1 |
| 41 to 48 | 0 |

**a** Estimate the mean average for the 8 year-olds.

**b** Estimate the mean average for the 18 year-olds.

**c** Compare the number of Christmas presents received by the 8 year-olds and the 18 year-olds.

# GEOMETRY 3

**11**

**TASK M11.1** ———————————————————— **Main Book Page 356**

**1** Measure these lines to the nearest tenth of a centimetre.

a _____    b _____

c _____

d _____

e

f

**2** Which shape below has the larger perimeter and by how much?

a     b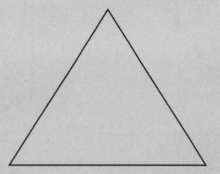

**3** Which shape below has the smaller perimeter and by how much?

a 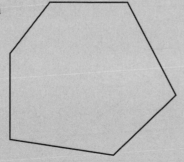    b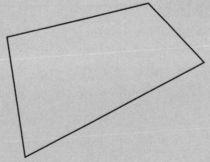

## TASK M11.2 — Main Book Page 357

*Using a protractor, measure the following angles.*

1
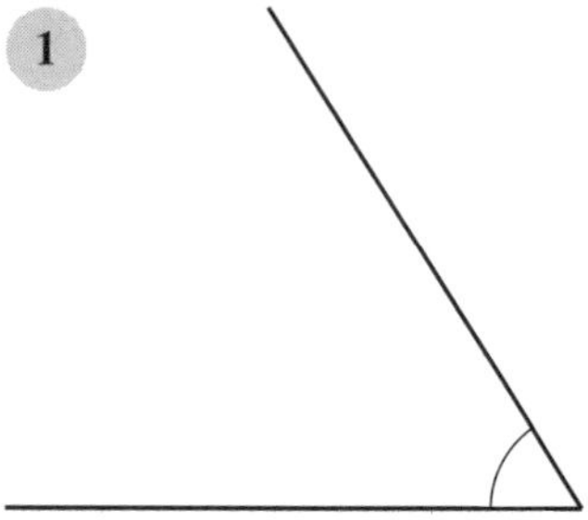

2
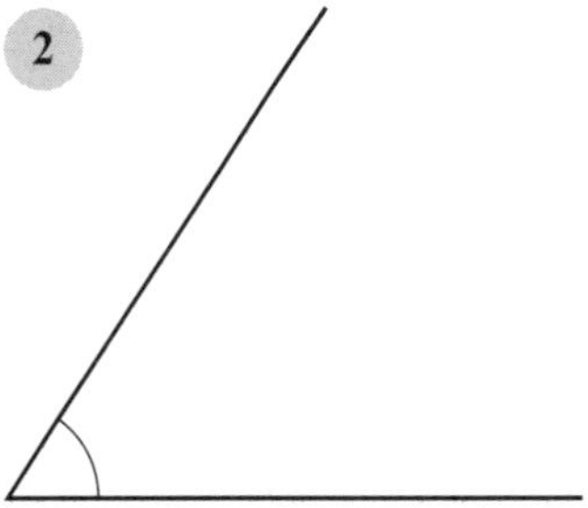

3
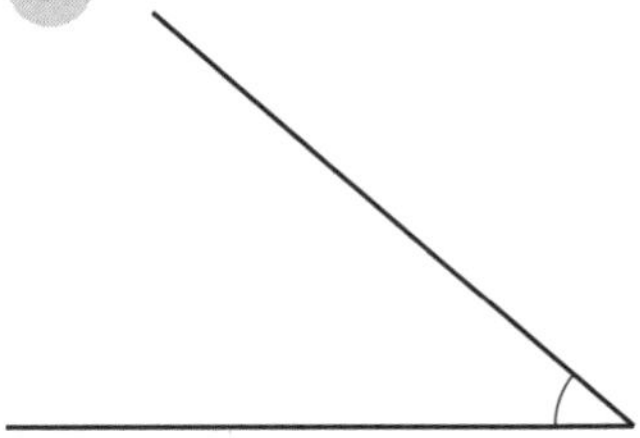

4
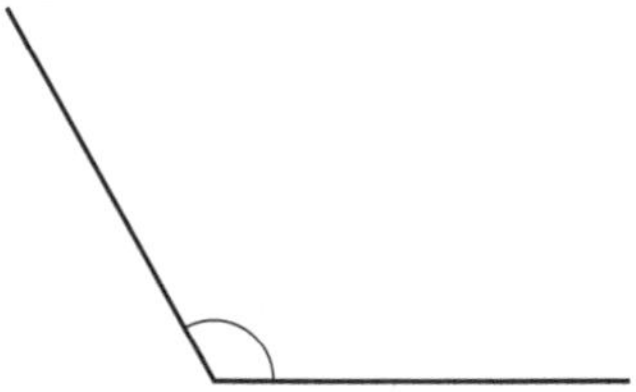

5
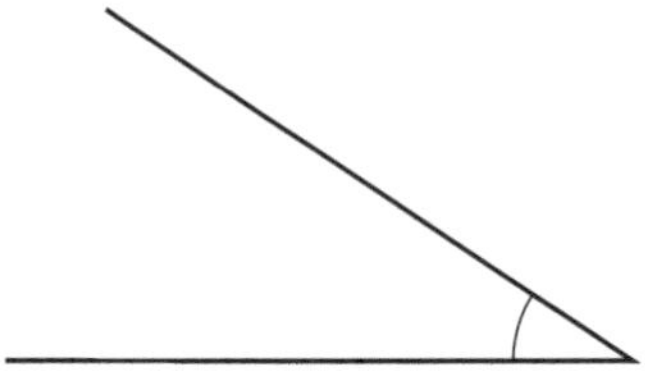

6
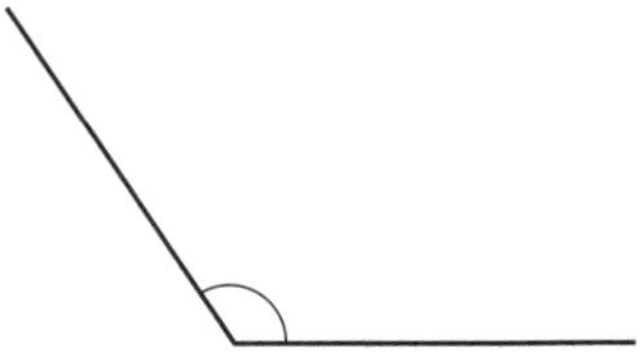

7
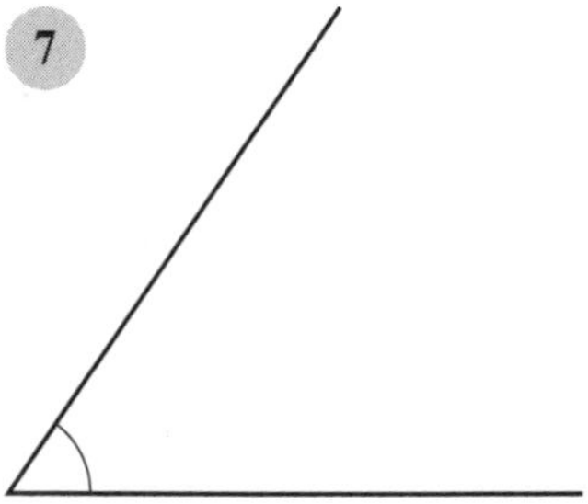

8
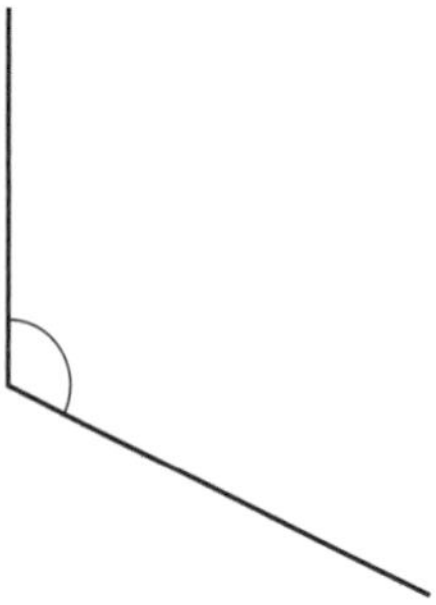

9
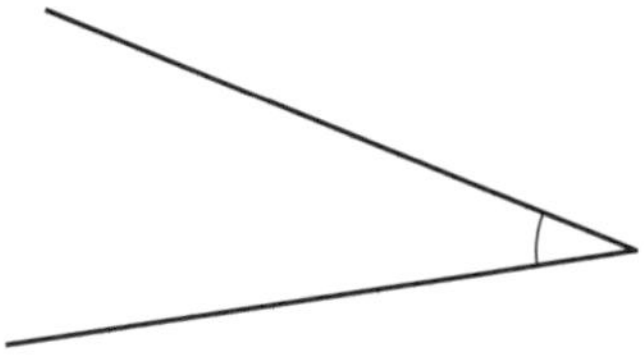

10 Use a protractor to draw the following angles. Label each angle acute, obtuse or reflex.

**a** 30° **b** 75° **c** 49° **d** 24°
**e** 135° **f** 113° **g** 157° **h** 18°

## TASK M11.3 — Main Book Page 358

1 Use a ruler and protractor to draw:

**a**
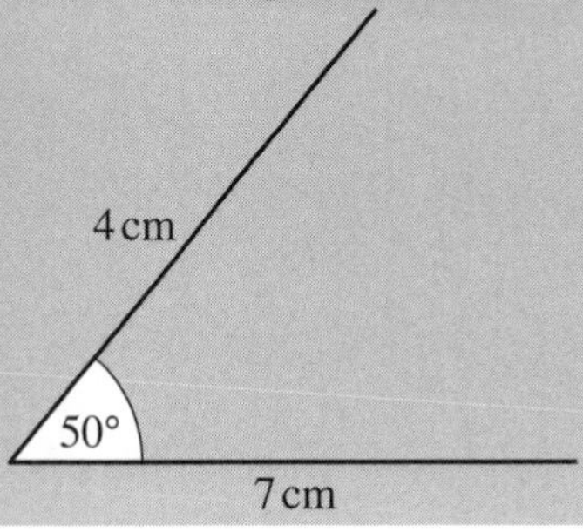
4 cm
50°
7 cm

**b**
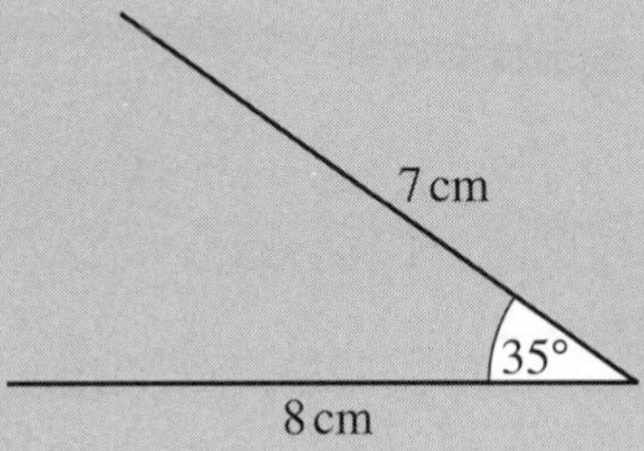
7 cm
35°
8 cm

**2**　**a** Draw accurately the triangle.

　　**b** Measure the length of the side marked $x$.

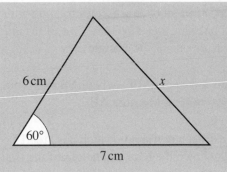

**3**　**a** Use a ruler and protractor to draw the triangle.

　　**b** Measure and write down angle $a$.

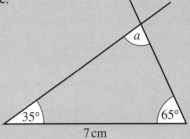

In questions **4** to **6**, construct the triangles and measure the lengths of the sides marked $x$.

**4**

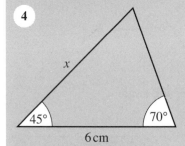

**5**

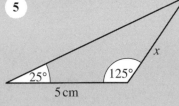

**6**

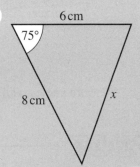

**TASK M11.4** ──────────────────── **Main Book Page 360**

In questions **1** to **3**, use a ruler and compasses only to draw each triangle.
Use a protractor to measure each angle $x$.

**1**

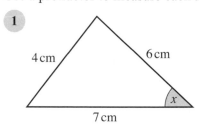

**2**

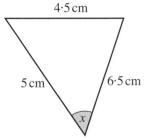

**3**

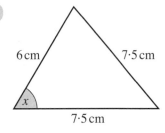

**4** Draw accurately an isosceles triangle with two sides equal to 5·5 cm
and one side equal to 7 cm. Two of the angles should be the same.
Measure one of these angles.

**5** Draw a triangle ABC, where AB = 5·2 cm, BC = 7·1 cm and
AC = 6·3 cm. Measure AB̂C.

**6** Construct any triangle which has area 15 cm².
Write down the base and height of the triangle.

**7** Construct a right-angled triangle with height 3 cm and area 6 cm².
Measure the perimeter of the triangle which should be 12 cm.

**8** Draw accurately the diagrams below:

**a**
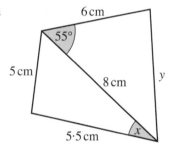

**b**
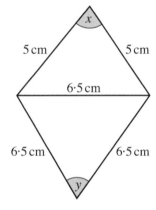

Measure angle *x* and side *y*.    Measure angle *x* and angle *y*.

---

**TASK M11.5** ──────────────────────── **Main Book Page 361**

Draw an accurate scale drawing of each shape below using the scale shown.

**1**
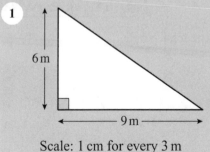

Scale: 1 cm for every 3 m

**2**
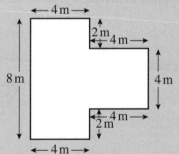

Scale: 1 cm for every 2 m

**3** Make a scale drawing of the front of this house using a scale of 1 cm for every 2 m.

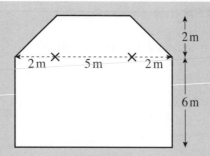

**4**

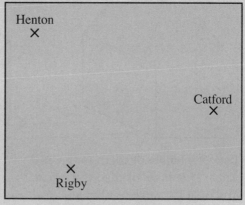

This is a plan of Rosemary's garden. It has been drawn to a scale of 1 cm for every 3 m.

**a** What is the length and width of the lawn? **b** How wide is the patio?

**c** What is the diameter of the pond? **d** What is the area of the vegeable patch?

**5** **a** How many km is Henton from Catford?
**b** How far is Catford from Rigby?
**c** How far is Henton from Rigby?

Henton
✗

Catford
✗

✗
Rigby

Scale: 1 cm for every 10 km

138

**1** Draw an accurate net for this cuboid.

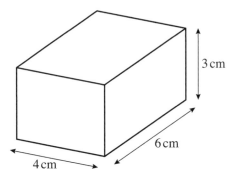

3 cm

6 cm

4 cm

**2** This net will fold to make a cube. Copy the net and put a cross X in the square which will be opposite the ● when the cube is made.

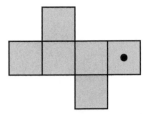

**3** This net makes a cuboid. What is the volume of the cuboid?

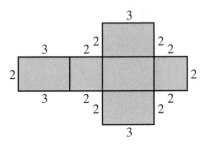

> **Remember:**
>
> volume of a
> cuboid = length $\times$ width $\times$ height

**4**

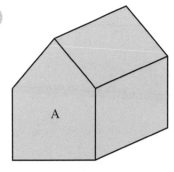

A

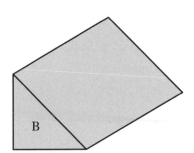

B

Let $n$ = number of edges for prism A
and $m$ = number of edges for prism B
Work out the value of $n^2 - m^2$.

**5** The two nets below will fold to make cuboids.
Each small square is 1 cm long.
Which cuboid has the greater volume and by how much?

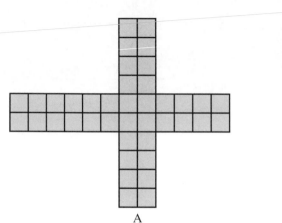

A

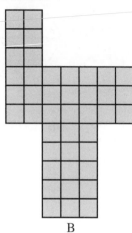

B

**6**

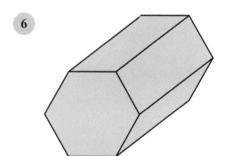

How many more edges
than vertices does this
prism have?

| **TASK E11.1** | **Main Book Page 364** |

**1** This is a tetrahedron (a triangular pyramid).

Which of these nets will make a tetrahedron?

A

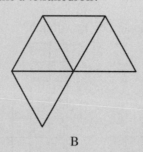

B

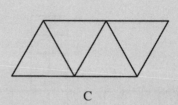

C

**2**  *Sketch* a net for this triangular prism.

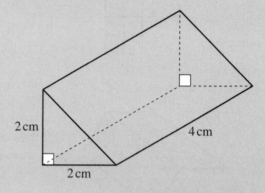

2 cm

2 cm

4 cm

**3**  *Sketch* a net for this solid (called an octahedron).

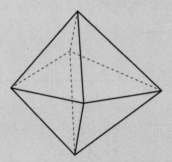

**4**  **a**  Draw a circle with radius 4 cm.

**b**  Keep the compasses set at 4 cm.
Place the compass point on the
circumference of the circle and
draw an arc across the circumference
as shown (A).

A

**c** Place the compass point on A and draw an arc across the circumference. Repeat the process right around the circumference as shown.

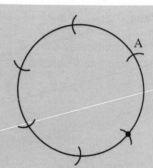

**d** Join the points as shown to make a hexagon.

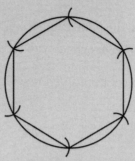

**e** Use *compasses* and a *ruler* to complete this net for a hexagonal-based pyramid.

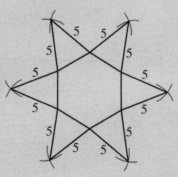

---

**TASK M11.7**                                                    **Main Book Page 365**

You will need isometric dot paper.

**1** Make a copy of each object below. For each drawing state the number of 'multilink' cubes needed to make the object.

**a**
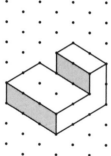

**b**
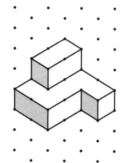

**2** Draw a cuboid with a volume of 12 cm³.

**3** How many more cubes are needed to make this shape into a cuboid?

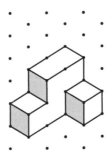

**4** **a** Draw a cuboid with length 8 cm, width 3 cm and height 1 cm.
   **b** Draw a *different* cuboid with the same volume.

**5** Draw this object from a *different view*.

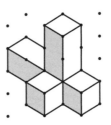

---

**TASK M11.8** ———————————————————— **Main Book Page 366**

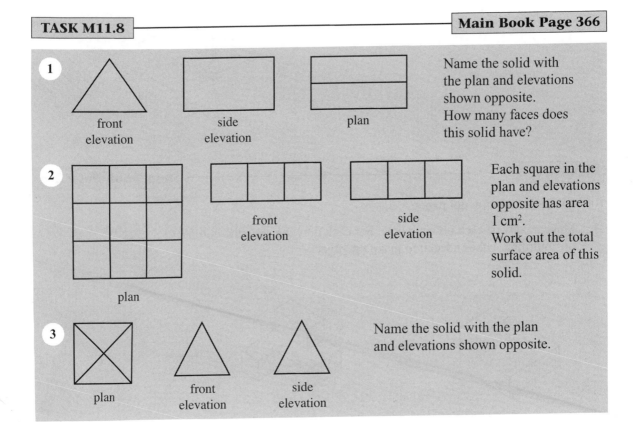

**1** 

front elevation    side elevation    plan

Name the solid with the plan and elevations shown opposite. How many faces does this solid have?

**2** 

plan    front elevation    side elevation

Each square in the plan and elevations opposite has area 1 cm². Work out the total surface area of this solid.

**3** 

plan    front elevation    side elevation

Name the solid with the plan and elevations shown opposite.

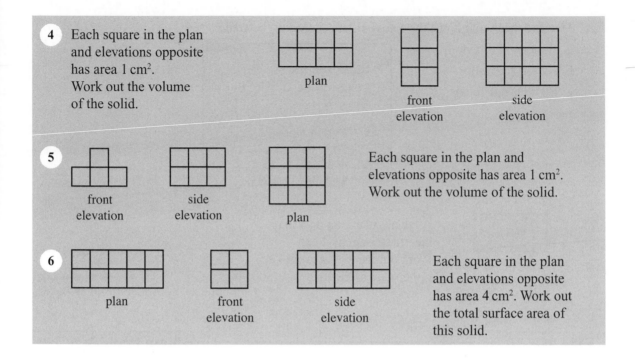

**4** Each square in the plan and elevations opposite has area 1 cm². Work out the volume of the solid.

plan

front elevation    side elevation

**5**

front elevation    side elevation    plan

Each square in the plan and elevations opposite has area 1 cm². Work out the volume of the solid.

**6**

plan    front elevation    side elevation

Each square in the plan and elevations opposite has area 4 cm². Work out the total surface area of this solid.

| TASK M11.9 | Main Book Page 368 |

**1** The model of a statue is made using a scale of 1 : 40.
If the statue is 3·2 m tall, how tall is the model (give your answer in cm)?

**2** A park is 5 cm long on a map whose scale is 1 : 40 000.
Find the actual length (in km) of the park.

**3** Copy and complete the table below.

| Map length | Scale | Real length |
|---|---|---|
| 7 cm | 1 : 60 | m |
| 5 cm | 1 : 2000 | m |
| 8 cm | 1 : 50 000 | km |
| cm | 1 : 100 000 | 3 km |
| cm | 1 : 4000 | 320 m |
| cm | 1 : 5 000 000 | 125 km |

**4** The distance between two towns is 25 km.
How far apart will they be on a map of scale 1 : 500 000?

**5** A plan of a house is made using a scale of 1 : 30. The width of the house on the plan is 40 cm.
What is the real width of the house? (Give your answer in metres.)

144

**6** Measure then write down the actual distances (in km) between:

    **a** Hatton and Bowton

    **b** Hatton and Tatley

    **c** Bowton and Tatley

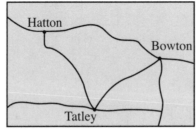

Scale is 1 : 200 000

**7** 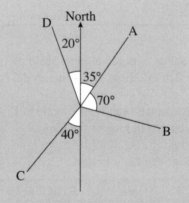 A rectangular area on a map measures 2 cm by 1 cm.
Work out the real area (in km²)
if the scale of the map is 1 : 500 000.

---

**TASK M11.10** ──────────────────────────── **Main Book Page 370**

**1** 4 rabbits escape from their run and race off in the directions shown.
On what bearing does each rabbit race?

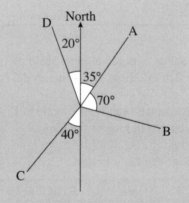

**Remember:**

a bearing is measured clockwise from the North

**2** The point at the centre is called M.
Find the bearing of:

    **a** P *from M*

    **b** S *from M*

    **c** R *from M*

    **d** T *from M*

    **e** Q *from M*

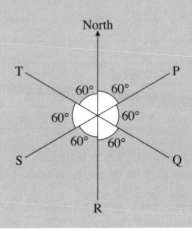

**3** Write down the bearing of:

**a** Barnworth  *from Hoston*
**b** Rigby  *from Hoston*
**c** Rigby  *from Barnworth*
**d** Hoston  *from Barnworth*
**e** Hoston  *from Rigby*

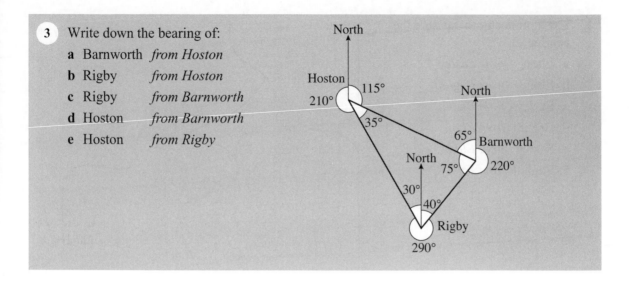

---

**TASK M11.11** ——————————————— **Main Book Page 371**

**1** Use a protractor to measure the bearing of:

**a** Harwich  *from Melton*
**b** Melton  *from Harwich*

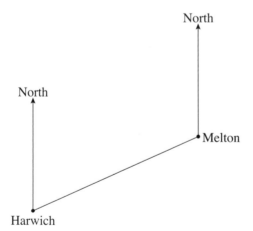

**2** Use a protractor to measure the bearing of:

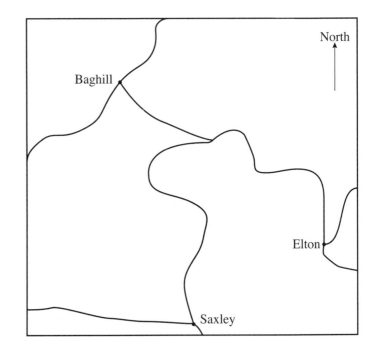

   **a** Elton   *from Saxley*

   **b** Elton   *from Baghill*

   **c** Saxley *from Baghill*

   **d** Baghill *from Elton*

   **e** Saxley *from Elton*

   **f** Baghill *from Saxley*

**3** 2 hikers walk 5 km due south and then 7 km on a bearing of 050°.

   **a** Use a scale of 1 cm for every 1 km to show their journey.

   **b** Find the distance of the hikers from their starting point.

**4** A submarine travels 40 km due north and then 65 km on a bearing of 300°.

   **a** Use a scale of 1 cm for every 10 km to show the submarine's journey.

   **b** Find the distance of the submarine from its starting point.

**5**

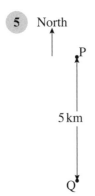

Two points P and Q are 5 km apart as shown opposite.
Q is due South of P.
Draw the points using a scale of 1 cm for every 1 km.
Rosie is on a bearing of 130° from P and on a bearing of 065° from Q.

   **a** Draw the position of Rosie.

   **b** Write down the bearing of Q from Rosie at this moment.

   **c** How far is Rosie from the point P?

**TASK M11.12** —————————————————

**1**  **a** Find the co-ordinates of the midpoint of line PQ.

**b** Copy the diagram opposite.

Draw in the point R at (6, 5).

**c** Work out the area of triangle PQR.

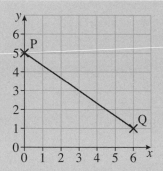

**2**  Write down the co-ordinates of the midpoint of the line joining (1, 3) to (5, 6).

**3**  Copy the grid.

Plot each set of co-ordinates below
in the order given to form two
sides of a rectangle.

Complete the rectangle and write
down the co-ordinates of the
missing vertex (corner).

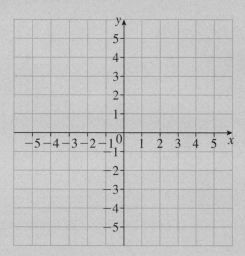

**a** $(2, 4), (2, -1), (4, -1), (\ \ , \ \ )$

**b** $(1, 1), (1, 3), (-4, 3), (\ \ , \ \ )$

**c** $(-1, -1), (-5, -1), (-5, -4), (\ \ , \ \ )$

**4**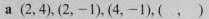

**a** Copy the diagram opposite.
Draw two more sides to make a kite.
Write down the co-ordinates of all
4 vertices of the kite.

**b** Work out the area of the kite.

**c** The point A is translated with $\binom{1}{0}$.

Work out the area of the new kite.

**5**  **a** Draw an $x$-axis from $-2$ to $6$ and $y$-axis from $-3$ to $3$.

**b** ABCD is a parallelogram. A is $(1, -2)$, B is $(-1, -2)$ and C is $(3, 2)$.
Draw the parallelogram.

**c** Write down the co-ordinates of D.

**d** Write down the co-ordinates of the midpoint of diagonal AC.